Laboratory Manual for
GENERAL MICROBIOLOGY
Laboratory Course MCB 2010L

Custom Edition for
Miami-Dade College (MDC) • North Campus
Department of Biology • Health and Wellness

Taken from:

Microbiology: A Laboratory Manual, Sixth Edition
by James G. Cappuccino and Natalie Sherman

Laboratory Experiments in Microbiology, Sixth Edition
by Ted R. Johnson and Christine L. Case

PEARSON
Custom
Publishing

PEARSON
Benjamin
Cummings

Cover photo courtesy of Photodisc/Getty Images, Inc.

Taken from:

Microbiology: A Laboratory Manual, Sixth Edition
by James G. Cappuccino and Natalie Sherman
Copyright © 2002 by Benjamin Cummings, Inc.
A Pearson Education Company
San Francisco, California 94111

Laboratory Experiments in Microbiology, Sixth Edition
by Ted R. Johnson and Christine L. Case
Copyright © 2001 by Benjamin Cummings, Inc.
A Pearson Education Company

Printed in the United States of America

27 28 29 30 31 V0UD 19 18 17 16 15

ISBN 0-536-26990-4

2006140255

EC

Please visit our web site at *www.pearsoncustom.com*

PEARSON CUSTOM PUBLISHING
75 Arlington Street, Suite 300, Boston, MA 02116
A Pearson Education Company

Laboratory Safety: General Guidelines

1. Notify your instructor immediately if you are pregnant, color blind, allergic to any insects or chemicals, taking immunosuppressive drugs, or have any other medical condition (such as diabetes, immunologic defect) that may require special precautionary measures in the laboratory.

2. Upon entering the laboratory, place all books, coats, purses, backpacks, etc. in designated areas, not on the bench tops.

3. Locate and, when appropriate, learn to use exits, fire extinguisher, fire blanket, chemical shower, eyewash, first aid kit, broken glass container, and cleanup materials for spills.

4. In case of fire, evacuate the room and assemble side the building.

5. Do not eat, drink, smoke, or apply cosmetics in the laboratory.

6. Confine long hair, loose clothing, and dangling jewelry.

7. Wear shoes at all times in the laboratory.

8. Cover any cuts or scrapes with a sterile, waterproof bandage before attending lab.

9. Wear eye protection when working with chemicals.

10. Never pipet by mouth. Use mechanical pipeting devices.

11. Wash skin immediately and thoroughly if contaminated by chemicals or microorganisms.

12. Do not perform unauthorized experiments.

13. Do not use equipment without instruction.

14. Report *all* spills and accidents to your instructor immediately.

15. Never leave heat sources unattended.

16. When using hot plates, note that there is no visible sign that they are hot (such as a red glow). Always assume that hot plates are hot.

17. Use an appropriate apparatus when handling hot glassware.

18. Keep chemicals away from direct heat or sunlight.

19. Keep containers of alcohol, acetone, and other flammable liquids away from flames.

20. Do not allow any liquid to come into contact with electrical cords. Handle electrical connectors with dry hands. Do not attempt to disconnect electrical equipment that crackles, snaps, or smokes.

21. Upon completion of laboratory exercises, place all materials in the disposal areas designated by your instructor.

22. Do not pick up broken glassware with your hands. Use a broom and dustpan and discard the glass in designated glass waste containers; never discard with paper waste.

23. Wear disposable gloves when working with blood, other body fluids, or mucous membranes. Change gloves after possible contamination and wash hands immediately after gloves are removed.

24. The disposal symbol indicates that items that may have come in contact with body fluids should be placed in your lab's designated container. It also refers to liquid wastes that should not be poured down the drain into the sewage system.

25. Leave the laboratory clean and organized for the next student.

26. Wash your hands with liquid or powdered soap prior to leaving the laboratory.

27. The biohazard symbol indicates procedures that may pose health concerns.

The caution symbol points out instruments, substances, and procedures that require special attention to safety. These symbols appear throughout this manual.

Measurement Conversions

Metric to American Standard	American Standard to Metric
Length	
1 mm = 0.039 inches	1 inch = 2.54 cm
1 cm = 0.394 inches	1 foot = 0.305 m
1 m = 3.28 feet	1 yard = 0.914 m
1 m = 1.09 yards	1 mile = 1.61 km
Volume	
1 mL = 0.0338 fluid ounces	1 fluid ounce = 29.6 mL
1 L = 4.23 cups	1 cup = 237 mL
1 L = 2.11 pints	1 pint = 0.474 L
1 L = 1.06 s	1 quart = 0.947 L
1 L = 0.264 gallons	1 gallon = 3.79 L
Mass	
1 mg = 0.0000353 ounces	1 ounce = 28.3 g
1 g = 0.0353 ounces	1 pound = 0.454 kg
1 kg = 2.21 pounds	

Temperature

To convert temperature:

$$°C = \frac{5}{9}(F - 32)$$

$$°F = \frac{9}{5}C + 32$$

°F | °C
- 230 — 110
- 220
- 210 — 100 ← Water boils
- 200
- 190 — 90
- 180 — 80
- 170
- 160 — 70
- 150
- 140 — 60
- 130
- 120 — 50
- 110
- — 40
98.6°F → ← 100 — 37°C
Normal human body temperature | Normal human body temperature
- 90 — 30
- 80
- 70 — 20
- 60
- 50 — 10
- 40
- 30 — 0 ← Water freezes
- 20
- 10 — −10
- 0
- — −20
- −10
- −20 — −30
- −30
- −40 — −40

Centimeters | Inches
- 20 — 8
- 19 — 7
- 18
- 17
- 16 — 6
- 15
- 14
- 13 — 5
- 12
- 11 — 4
- 10
- 9
- 8 — 3
- 7
- 6
- 5 — 2
- 4
- 3 — 1
- 2
- 1
- 0 — 0

Contents

BACTERIAL MOTILITY TEST: "HANGING-DROP" EXPERIMENT

STAINS AND BACTERIAL STAINING

STRUCTURAL STAINING: ENDOSPORE AND CAPSULE STAINS

MICROBIAL PHYSIOLOGY: BACTERIAL GROWTH CURVE

CONTROL OF MICROBIAL GROWTH AND ACTIVITY

ANTIBIOTIC SENSITIVITY TEST

PUBLIC HEALTH MICROBIOLOGY

BACTERIAL IDENTIFICATION: FERMENTATIONS

TESTS FOR STARCH, GELATIN, CASEIN, AND LIPID HYDROLYSIS

BACTERIAL IDENTIFICATION: BIOCHEMICAL TESTS

INDOLE PRODUCTION, METHYL RED, VOGES PROSKAUER, AND CITRATE UTILIZATION TESTS

INDUSTRIAL MICROBIOLOGY: HOW TO MAKE YOGURT

1

Laboratory Safety:
General Rules and Regulations

A rewarding laboratory experience demands strict adherence to prescribed rules for personal and environmental safety. The former reflects concern for your personal safety in terms of avoiding laboratory accidents. The latter requires that you maintain a scrupulously clean laboratory setting to prevent contamination of experimental procedures by microorganisms from exogenous sources.

Because most microbiological laboratory procedures require the use of living organisms, an integral part of all laboratory sessions is the use of aseptic techniques. Although the virulence of microorganisms used in the academic laboratory environment has been greatly diminished because of their ιg-term maintenance on artificial media, ___l **microorganisms should be treated as potential pathogens** (organisms capable of producing disease). Thus, microbiology students must develop aseptic techniques (free of contaminating organisms) in the preparation of pure cultures that are essential in the industrial and clinical marketplaces.

The following basic steps should be observed at all times to reduce the ever-present microbial flora of the laboratory environment.

1. Upon entering the laboratory, place coats, books, and other paraphernalia in specified locations—never on bench tops.

2. Keep doors and windows closed during the laboratory session to prevent contamination from air currents.

3. At the beginning and termination of each laboratory session, wipe bench tops with a disinfectant solution provided by the instructor.

4. Do not place contaminated instruments, such as inoculating loops, needles, and pipettes, on bench tops. Loops and needles should be sterilized by incineration, and pipettes should be disposed of in designated receptacles.

5. On completion of the laboratory session, place all cultures and materials in the disposal area as designated by the instructor.

6. Rapid and efficient manipulation of fungal cultures is required to prevent the dissemination of their reproductive spores in the laboratory environment.

To prevent accidental injury and infection of yourself and others, observe the following regulations at all times:

1. Wash your hands with liquid detergent and dry them with paper towels upon entering and prior to leaving the laboratory.

2. Wear a paper cap or tie back long hair to minimize its exposure to open flames.

3. Wear a laboratory coat or apron while working in the laboratory to protect clothing from contamination or accidental discoloration by staining solutions.

4. Closed shoes should be worn at all times in the laboratory setting.

5. Never apply cosmetics or insert contact lenses in the laboratory.

6. Do not smoke, eat, or drink in the laboratory. These activities are absolutely prohibited.

7. Carry cultures in a test-tube rack when moving around the laboratory. Likewise, keep cultures in a test-tube rack on the bench tops when not in use. This serves a dual purpose: to prevent accidents and to avoid contamination of yourself and the environment.

8. Never remove media, equipment, or especially, **bacterial cultures** from the laboratory. Doing so is absolutely prohibited.

9. Immediately cover spilled cultures or broken culture tubes with paper towels and then saturate them with disinfectant

From *Microbiology: A Laboratory Manual*, Sixth Edition, James G. Cappuccino and Natalie Sherman. Copyright © 2002 Pearson Education, Inc., publishing as Benjamin Cummings. All rights reserved.

solution. After 15 minutes of reaction time, remove the towels and dispose of them in a manner indicated by the instructor.

10. Report accidental cuts or burns to the instructor immediately.

11. Never pipette by mouth any broth cultures or chemical reagents. Doing so is strictly prohibited. Pipetting is to be carried out with the aid of a mechanical pipetting device only.

12. Do not lick labels. Use only self-stick labels for the identification of experimental cultures.

13. Speak quietly and avoid unnecessary movement around the laboratory to prevent distractions that may cause accidents.

The following specific precautions must be observed when handling body fluids of unknown origin due to the possible imminent transmission of the HIV and hepatitis B viruses in these test specimens.

1. Disposable gloves must be worn during the manipulation of these test materials.

2. Immediate hand washing is required if contact with any of these fluids occurs and also upon removal of the gloves.

3. Masks, safety goggles, and laboratory coats should be worn if an aerosol might be formed or splattering of these fluids is likely to occur.

4. Spilled body fluids should be decontaminated with a 1:10 dilution of household bleach, covered with paper toweling, and allowed to react for 10 minutes before removal.

5. Test specimens and supplies in contact with these fluids must be placed into a container of disinfectant prior to autoclaving.

I have read the above laboratory safety rules and regulations and agree to abide by them.

_____

Name   Date

Laboratory Safety: General Rules and Regulations

Laboratory Protocol

Student Preparation for Laboratory Sessions

The efficient performance of laboratory exercises mandates that you attend each session fully prepared to execute the required procedures. Read the assigned experimental protocols to effectively plan and organize the related activities. This will allow you to maximize use of laboratory time.

Preparation of Experimental Materials

Microscope Slides: Meticulously clean slides are essential for microscopic work. Commercially precleaned slides should be used for
ch microscopic slide preparation. However, wipe these slides with dry lens paper to remove dust and finger marks prior to their use. With a glassware marking pencil, label one end of each slide with the abbreviated name of the organism to be viewed.

Labeling of Culture Vessels: Generally, microbiological experiments require the use of a number of different test organisms and a variety of culture media. To ensure the successful completion of experiments, organize all experimental cultures and sterile media at the start of each experiment. Label culture vessels with non–water-soluble glassware markers and/or self-stick labels prior to their inoculation. The labeling on each of the experimental vessels should include the name of the test organism, the name of the medium, the dilution of sample (if any), your name or initials, and the date. **Place labeling directly below the cap of the culture tube.** When labeling Petri dish cultures, only the name of the organism(s) should be written on the bottom of the plate, close to its periphery, to prevent obscuring observation of the results. The additional information for the identification of the culture should be written on the cover of the Petri dish.

Inoculation Procedures

Aseptic techniques for the transfer or isolation of microorganisms, using the necessary transfer instruments, are described fully in the experiments in Part I of the manual. Technical skill will be acquired through repetitive practice.

Inoculating Loops and Needles: It is imperative that you incinerate the entire wire to ensure absolute sterilization. The shaft should also be briefly passed through the flame to remove any dust or possible contaminants. To avoid killing the cells and splattering the culture, cool the inoculating wire by tapping the inner surface of the culture tube or the Petri dish cover prior to obtaining the inoculum.

When performing an aseptic transfer of microorganisms, a minute amount of inoculum is required. If an agar culture is used, touch only a single area of growth with the inoculating wire to obtain the inoculum. **Never drag the loop or needle over the entire surface, and take care not to dig into the solid medium.** If a broth medium is used, first tap the bottom of the tube against the palm of your hand to suspend the microorganisms. **Caution:** Do not tap the culture vigorously as this may cause spills or excessive foaming of the culture, which may denature the proteins in the medium.

Pipettes: Use only sterile, disposable pipettes or glass pipettes sterilized in a canister. The practice of **pipetting by mouth has been discontinued** to eliminate the possibility of autoinfection by the accidental imbibement of the culture or infectious body fluids. Instead, a mechanical pipetting device is to be used to obtain and deliver the material to be inoculated.

Incubation Procedure

Microorganisms exhibit a wide temperature range for growth. However, for most used in this manual, optimum growth occurs at 37°C over a period of 18 to 24 hours. Unless otherwise indicated in specific exercises, incubate all cultures under the conditions cited above. Place culture tubes in a rack for incubation. Petri dishes may be stacked; however, they **must always be incubated in an inverted position (top down)** to prevent water from condensation from dropping onto the surface of the culture medium. This resultant excess moisture may then serve as a vehicle for the spread of the microorganisms on the surface of the culture medium, thereby producing confluent rather than discrete   bial growth.

Procedure for Recording Observations and Results

The accurate accumulation of experimental data is essential for the critical interpretation of the observations upon which the final results will be based. To achieve this end, it is imperative that you complete all the preparatory readings that are necessary for your understanding of the basic principles underlying each experiment. Meticulously record all the observed data in the "Observations and Results" section of each experiment.

In the exercises that require drawings to illustrate microbial morphology, it will be advantageous to depict shapes, arrangements, and cellular structures enlarged to 5 to 10 times their actual microscopic size, as illustrated below. For this purpose a number 2 pencil is preferable. Stippling may be

used to depict different aspects of cell structure (e.g., endospores or differences in staining density).

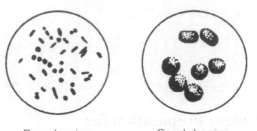

Poor drawing   Good drawing

Review Questions

The review questions are designed to evaluate student's understanding of the principles and the interpretations of observations in each experiment. Completion of these questions will also serve to reinforce many of the concepts that are discussed in the lectures. At times, this will require the use of ancillary sources such as textbooks, microbiological reviews, or abstracts. The designated critical-thinking questions are designed to stimulate further refinement of cognitive skills.

Procedure for Termination of Laboratory Sessions

1. All equipment, supplies, and chemical reagents are to be returned to their original locations.

2. All capped test-tube cultures and closed Petri dishes are to be neatly placed in a designated collection area in the laboratory for subsequent autoclaving.

3. Contaminated materials, such as swabs, disposable pipettes, and paper towels, are to be placed in a biohazard receptacle prior to autoclaving.

4. Hazardous biochemicals, such as potential carcinogens, are to be carefully placed into a sealed container and stored in a fume hood prior to their disposal according to the institutional policy.

5. Wipe down table top with recommended disinfectant.

6. Wash hands before leaving the laboratory.

2

Microscopic Examination of Stained Cell Preparations

PURPOSES

To become familiar with the

1. Theoretical principles of brightfield micros-copy.
2. Component parts of the compound microscope.
3. Use and care of the compound microscope.
4. Practical use of the compound microscope for visualization of cellular morphology from stained slide preparations.

RINCIPLE

Microbiology is a science that studies living organisms that are too small to be seen with the naked eye. Needless to say, such a study must involve the use of a good compound microscope. Although there are many types and variations, they all fundamentally consist of a two- lens system, a variable but controllable light source, and mechanical adjustable parts for determining focal length between the lenses and specimen (Figure 1).

Components of the Microscope

Stage A fixed platform with an opening in the center allows the passage of light from an illuminating source below to the lens system above the stage. This platform provides a surface for the placement of a slide with its specimen over the central opening. In addition to the fixed stage, most microscopes have a **mechanical stage** that can be moved vertically or horizontally by means of adjustment controls. Less sophisticated microscopes have clips on the fixed stage, and the slide must be positioned manually over the central opening.

Illumination The light source is positioned in the base of the instrument. Some micro-

scopes are equipped with a built-in light source to provide direct illumination. Others are provided with a reversible mirror that has one side flat and the other concave. An external light source, such as a lamp, is placed in front of the mirror to direct the light upward into the lens system. The flat side of the mirror is used for artificial light, and the concave side for sunlight.

Abbé Condenser This component is found directly under the stage and contains two sets of lenses that collect and concentrate light as it passes upward from the light source into the lens systems. The condenser is equipped with an **iris diaphragm**, a shutter controlled by a lever that is used to regulate the amount of light entering the lens system.

Body Tube Above the stage and attached to the arm of the microscope is the body tube. This structure houses the lens system that magnifies the specimen. The upper end of the tube contains the **ocular** or **eyepiece** lens. The lower portion consists of a movable **nosepiece** containing the **objective lenses**. Rotation of the nosepiece positions objectives above the stage opening. The body tube may be raised or lowered with the aid of **coarse-adjustment** and **fine-adjustment knobs** that are located above or below the stage, depending on the type and make of the instrument.

Theoretical Principles of Microscopy

To use the microscope efficiently and with minimal frustration, you should understand the basic principles of microscopy: magnification, resolution, numerical aperture, illumination, and focusing.

Magnification Enlargement, or magnification, of a specimen is the function of a two-lens system; the **ocular lens** is found in the eyepiece, and the **objective lens** is situated in

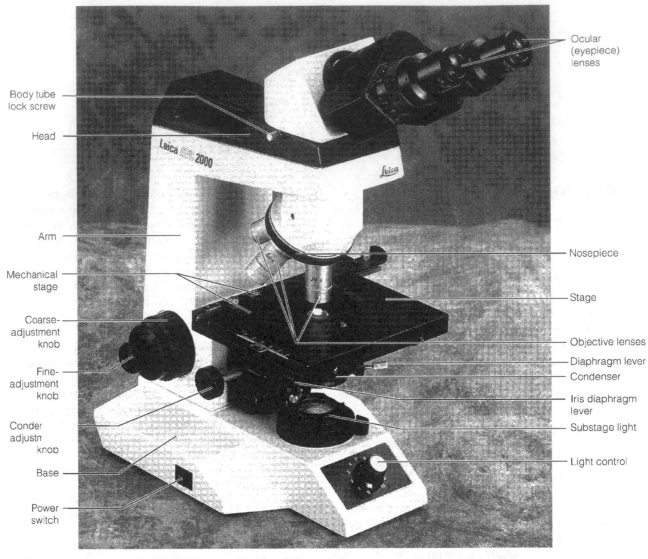

Body tube lock screw

Head

Arm

Mechanical stage

Coarse-adjustment knob

Fine-adjustment knob

Conder adjustm knob

Base

Power switch

Ocular (eyepiece) lenses

Nosepiece

Stage

Objective lenses

Diaphragm lever

Condenser

Iris diaphragm lever

Substage light

Light control

FIGURE 1   Leica ATC 2000 compound microscope (Courtesy of Leica Microsystems, Inc.)

a revolving nosepiece. These lenses are separated by the **body tube**. The objective lens is nearer the specimen and magnifies it, producing the **real image** that is projected up into the focal plane and then magnified by the ocular lens to produce the final image.

The most commonly used microscopes are equipped with a revolving nosepiece containing four objective lenses, each possessing a different degree of magnification. When these are combined with the magnification of the ocular lens, the total or overall linear magnification of the specimen is obtained. This is shown in Table 1.

Resolving Power or Resolution Although magnification is important, you must be aware that unlimited enlargement is not possible by merely increasing the magnifying power of the lenses or by using additional lenses, because lenses are limited by a property called **resolving power**. By definition, resolving power is the ability of a lens to show two adjacent objects as discrete entities. When a lens cannot discriminate, that is, when the two objects appear as one, it has lost resolution. Increased magnification will not rectify the loss and will, in fact, blur the object. The resolving power of a lens is dependent on the wavelength of light used and

TABLE 1 Overall Linear Magnification

Magnification		Total Magnification
Objective Lenses	Ocular Lens	Objective Multiplied by Ocular
Scanning 4 ×	10×	40×
Low-power 10 ×	10×	100×
High-power 45 ×	10×	450×
Oil-immersion 97 ×	10×	970×

the **numerical aperture**, which is a characteristic of each lens and imprinted on each objective. The numerical aperture is defined as a function of the diameter of the objective lens in relation to its focal length. It is doubled by use of the substage condenser, which illuminates the object with rays of light that pass through the specimen obliquely as well as directly. Thus, resolving power is expressed mathematically, as follows:

$$\text{Resolving power} = \frac{\text{Wavelength of light}}{2 \times \text{numerical aperture}}$$

Based on this formula, the shorter the wavelength, the greater the resolving power of the lens. Thus, for the same numerical aperture, short wavelengths of the electromagnetic spectrum are better suited for higher resolution than are longer wavelengths.

However, as with magnification, resolving power also has limits. You might rationalize that merely decreasing the wavelength will automatically increase the resolving power of a lens. Such is not the case, because the visible portion of the electromagnetic spectrum is very narrow and borders on the very short wavelengths found in the ultraviolet portion of the spectrum.

The relationship between wavelength and numerical aperture is valid only for increased resolving power when light rays are parallel. Therefore, the resolving power is also dependent on another factor, the **refractive index**. This is the bending power of light passing through air from the glass slide to the objective lens. The refractive index of air is lower than that of glass; as light rays pass from the glass slide into the air, they are bent or refracted so that they do not pass into the objective lens. This would cause a loss of light, which would reduce the numerical aperture and diminish the resolving power of the objective lens. Loss of refracted light can be compensated for by

interposing mineral oil, which has the same refractive index as glass, between the slide and the objective lens. In this way, decreased light refraction occurs and more light rays enter directly into the objective lens, producing a vivid image with high resolution (Figure 2).

Illumination Effective illumination is required for efficient magnification and resolving power. Since the intensity of daylight is an uncontrolled variable, artificial light from a tungsten lamp is the most commonly used light source in microscopy. The light is

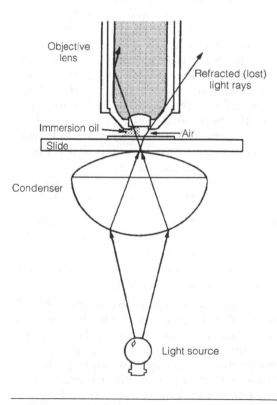

FIGURE 2 Refractive index in air and mineral oil

Microscopic Examination of Stained Cell Preparations

passed through the condenser located beneath the stage. The condenser contains two lenses that are necessary to produce a maximum numerical aperture. The height of the condenser can be adjusted with the **condenser knob**. Always keep the condenser close to the stage, especially when using the oil-immersion objective.

Between the light source and the condenser is the iris diaphragm, which can be opened and closed by means of a lever, thereby regulating the amount of light entering the condenser. Excessive illumination may actually obscure the specimen because of lack of contrast. The amount of light entering the microscope differs with each objective lens used. A rule of thumb is that **as the magnification of the lens increases, the distance between the objective lens and slide, called working distance, decreases, whereas the numerical aperture of the objective lens increases** (Figure 3).

Use and Care of the Microscope

You will be responsible for the proper care and use of microscopes. Since microscopes are expensive, you must observe the following ｜lations and procedures.

Th ｜struments are housed in special cabinets and must be moved by users to their laboratory benches. The correct and only acceptable way to do this is to grip the microscope arm firmly with the right hand and the base with the left hand, and lift the instrument from the cabinet shelf. Carry it close to the body and gently place it on the laboratory bench. This will prevent collision with furniture or coworkers and will protect the instrument against damage.

Once the microscope is placed on the laboratory bench, observe the following rules:

1. Remove all unnecessary materials (such as books, papers, purses, and hats) from the laboratory bench.
2. Uncoil the microscope's electric cord and plug it into an electrical outlet.
3. Clean all lens systems; the smallest bit of dust, oil, lint, or eyelash will decrease the efficiency of the microscope. The ocular, scanning, low-power, and high-power lenses may be cleaned by wiping several times with acceptable lens tissue. Never use paper toweling or cloth on a lens surface. If the oil-immersion lens is gummy or tacky, a piece of lens paper

moistened with xylol is used to wipe it clean. The xylol is immediately removed with a tissue moistened with 95% alcohol, and the lens is wiped dry with lens paper. **This xylol cleansing procedure should be performed only by the instructor and only if necessary**; consistent use of xylol may loosen the lens.

The following routine procedures must be followed to ensure correct and efficient use of the microscope.

1. Place the microscope slide with the specimen within the stage clips on the fixed stage. Move the slide to center the specimen over the opening in the stage directly over the light source.
2. Rotate the scanning lens or low-power lens into position. Lower the body tube with the coarse-adjustment knob to its lowest position. **Never lower the body tube while looking through the ocular lens.**
3. While looking through the ocular lens, use the coarse-adjustment knob to slowly raise the stage until the specimen comes into focus. Using the fine-adjustment knob, bring the specimen into sharp focus.
4. Adjust the substage condenser to achieve optimal focus.
5. Routinely adjust the light source by means of the light-source transformer setting, and/or the iris diaphragm, for optimum illumination for each new slide and for each change in magnification.
6. Most microscopes are **par focal**, which means that when one lens is in focus, other lenses will also have the same focal length and can be rotated into position without further major adjustment. In practice, however, usually a half-turn of the fine-adjustment knob in either direction is necessary for sharp focus.
7. Once you have brought the specimen into sharp focus with a low-powered lens, preparation may be made for visualizing the specimen under oil immersion. Place a drop of oil on the slide directly over the area to be viewed. Rotate the nosepiece until the oil-immersion objective locks into position. **Care should be taken not to allow the high-power objective to touch the drop of oil.** The slide is observed from the side as the objective is

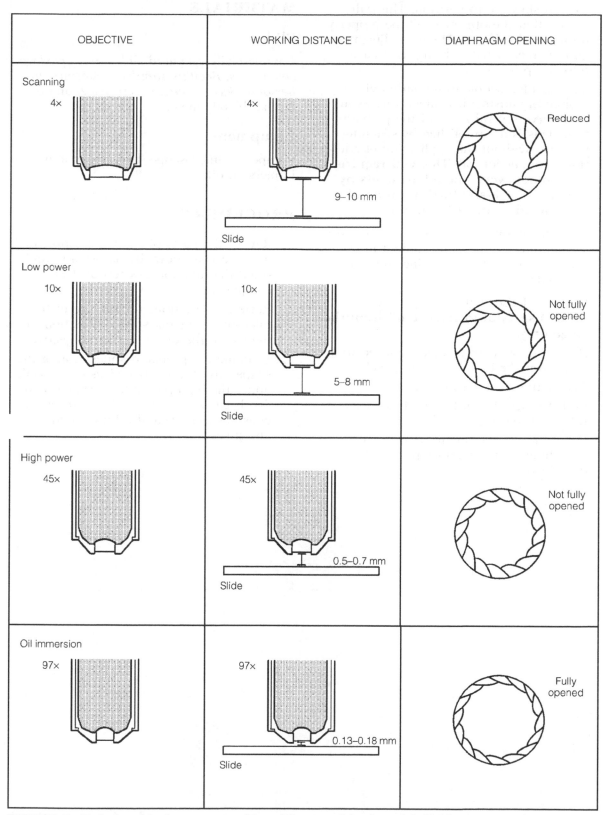

FIGURE 3 Relationship between working distance objective and diaphragm opening

Microscopic Examination of Stained Cell Preparations

rotated slowly into position. This will ensure that the objective will be properly immersed in the oil. The fine-adjustment knob is readjusted to bring the image into sharp focus.

8. During microscopic examination of microbial organisms, it is always necessary to observe several areas of the preparation. This is accomplished by scanning the slide without the application of additional immersion oil. **This will require continuous, very fine adjustments by the slow, back-and-forth rotation of the fine-adjustment knob only.**

On completion of the laboratory exercise, return the microscope to its cabinet in its original condition. The following steps are recommended:

1. Clean all lenses with dry, clean lens paper. **Use xylol to remove oil from the stage only.**
2. Place the low-power objective in position and lower the body tube completely.
3. Center the mechanical stage.
4. Coil the electric cord around the body tube and the stage.
5. Ca....e microscope to its position in its cabinet in the manner previously described.

MATERIALS

Slides

Commercially prepared slides of *Staphylococcus aureus*, *Bacillus subtilis*, *Aquaspirillum itersonii*, *Saccharomyces cerevisiae*, and a human blood smear.

Equipment

Compound microscope, lens paper, and immersion oil.

PROCEDURE

1. Review the parts of the microscope, making sure you know the names and understand the function of each of these components.
2. Review instructions for the use of the microscope, giving special attention to the use of the oil-immersion objective.
3. Examine the prepared slides, noting the shapes and the relative sizes of the cells under the high-power (also called high-dry, because it is the highest power that does not use oil) and oil-immersion objectives.

Name   Section   Date

OBSERVATIONS AND RESULTS

In the chart provided
1. Draw several cells from a typical microscopic field as viewed under each magnification.
2. Give the total magnification for each objective.

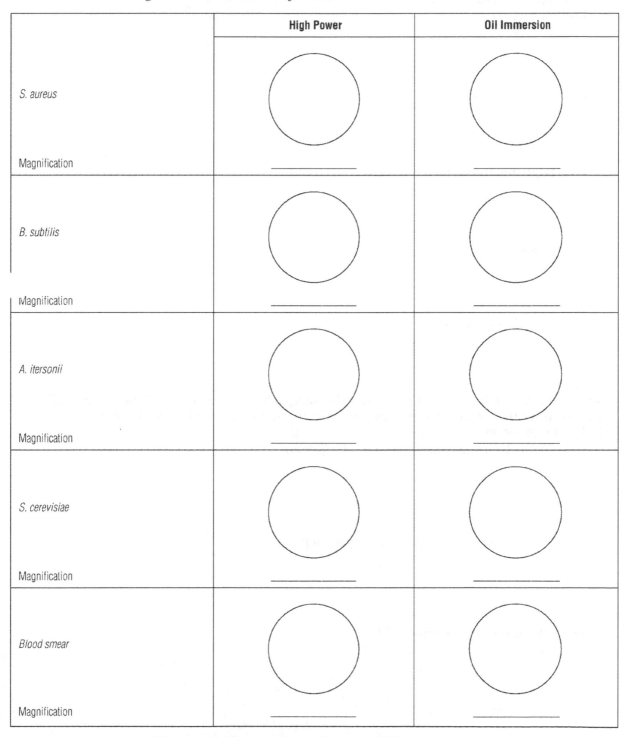

	High Power	Oil Immersion
S. aureus		
Magnification		
B. subtilis		
Magnification		
A. itersonii		
Magnification		
S. cerevisiae		
Magnification		
Blood smear		
Magnification		

Microscopic Examination of Stained Cell Preparations

REVIEW QUESTIONS

1. Explain why the body tube of the microscope should not be lowered while you are looking through the ocular lens.

2. For what purpose would you adjust each of the following microscope components during a microscopy exercise?

   a. Iris diaphragm:

   b. Coarse-adjustment knob:

   c. Fine-adjustment knob:

   d. Condenser:

   e. Mechanical stage control:

3. As a beginning student in the microbiology laboratory, you experience some difficulties in using the oil-immersion lens. Describe the steps you would take to correct the following problems:

   a. Inability to bring the specimen into sharp focus.

   b. Insufficient light while viewing the specimen.

   c. Artifacts in the microscopic field.

3

MICROBIAL DIVERSITY AND
SURVEY OF MICROBIAL LIFE

OBJECTIVES

1. Explore diversity of Microbial life
2. Use prepared slides to survey different kinds of microbes
3. Compare characteristics of various microorganisms
4. Examine different cell-types in microorganisms
5. Sort microorganisms into taxonomic groups

INTRODUCTION

Microorganisms make up the vast majority of life-forms and they come in different shapes and sizes. The key factors that unite microbes are their extremely small sizes and simple design. Therefore, they are studied with a microscope. Microorganisms show great diversity of forms; of six Kingdoms of life, four (Archaea, Eubacteria, Protista, and Fungi) include microorganisms:

- Some have prokaryotic cells, others have eukaryotic cells;
- Some have cell walls, others lack cell walls;
- Some are unicellular, others are multicellular;
- Some are simple multicellular, others are complex multicellular;
- Nutritionally, some are autotrophs, others are heterotrophs;
- Some live freely in water, on land, or in the air, others are parasitic;
- Some have characteristics of animals, others look like plants.

PURPOSE

In this Exercise, you will explore the diversity of microbial life by viewing prepared slides that have been carefully selected to showcase different microbial types. The list on the next page shows microorganisms sorted into categories by their characteristics.

MATERIALS

Before viewing a slide, refer to the Reference Photographic Atlas on your Table and the page indicated for each microorganism on the list. This will give you an idea of what your specimen may look like before you actually see them with a microscope.

The first slides on the list are intended for Exercise 2. All other slides have specimens for Exercise 3. Other sections of this Exercise also include additional information about how to prepare your own slides and enhance your understanding of:

- The Protozoa
- Free-Living Protozoa
- Phototrophs: Algae and Cyanobacteria
- Fungi

However, note that you are not required to prepare your own slides for this Exercise.

SLIDE NUMBER	NAME OF SPECIMEN	RECOMMENDED OBJECTIVE LENS	IMMERSION OIL REQUIRED?	ATLAS PAGE REFERENCE
SLIDES FOR EXERCISE 2 ONLY (MICROSCOPY)				
1.	Graph & Letter Slide	X4; x10	No	N/A
2.	Cross Fibers from Cloth	X4; X10	No	N/A
PROKARYOTIC MICROORGANIMS				
BACTERIA				
3.	Bacterial Types	X4; X10; X40; X100	Yes, must use X100	28; Fig. 3:14-18
CYANOBACTERIA – Photosynthetic Bacteria				
4.	Oscillatoria	X10 up toX100	Yes, if X100 is used	26; Fig. 3:6
5.	Nostoc	X10 up toX100	Yes, if X100 is used	25; Fig. 3:2; 3:4
EUKARYOTIC MICROORGANIMS				
PROTISTA P rotozoa				
6.	*Amoeba proteus*	X4 up to X40	No	31; Fig. 4:10
7.	*Paramecium*	X4 up to X40	No	34; Fig. 4:20
8.	*Euglena*	X10 up to X100	Yes, if X100 is used	33; Fig. 4:16-18
PROTISTA Alg ae				
9.	*Volvox*	X10 up to X40	No	35; 4:25-27
10.	*Spirogyra*	X10 up to X40	No	37; Fig. 4:37
PROTISTA S lime molds				
11.	*Saprolegnia*	X4 up to X40	No	44; Fig. 4:65-66
FUNGI				
12.	*Rhizopus*	X4 up to X10	No	47; Fig. 5:3-6
13.	*Coprinus*	X4 up to X40	No	54; Fig. 4:27
14.	*Penicillium*	X10 or X40	No	51; Fig. 4:16-17

The Protozoa

PURPOSES

1. To become familiar with the distinguishing characteristics of the members of the phylum Protozoa.
2. To perform experimental procedures to identify free-living and parasitic protozoans.

INTRODUCTION

The protozoa are a large and diverse group of unicellular, eukaryotic organisms. Most are free-living, but some are parasites. Their major distinguishing characteristics are:

1. The absence of a cell wall; some, however, possess a flexible layer, a pellicle, or a rigid shell of inorganic materials outside of the cell membrane.
2. The ability during their entire life cycle or part of it to move by locomotor organelles or by a gliding mechanism.
3. Heterotrophic nutrition whereby the free-living forms ingest particulates such as bacteria, yeast, and algae, while the parasitic forms derive nutrients from the body fluids of their hosts.
4. Primarily asexual means of reproduction, although sexual modes occur in some groups.

Taxonomically, the classification of protozoa depends on their means of locomotion in the mature stage. The phylum is subdivided into the following four classes (or subphyla, according to some taxonomists):

1. **Sarcodina:** Motility results from the streaming of ectoplasm, producing protoplasmic projections called pseudopods (false feet). Prototypic amoebas include the free-living *Amoeba proteus* and its parasitic congener *Entamoeba histolytica*.
2. **Mastigophora:** Locomotion is effected by one or more whiplike, thin structures called flagella. Free-living members include the genera *Cercomonas*, *Heteronema*, and *Euglena*, which are photosynthetic protists that may be classified as flagellated algae. The parasitic forms include *Trichomonas vaginalis*, *Giardia lamblia*, and the *Trypanosoma* species.
3. **Ciliophora:** Locomotion is carried out by means of short hairlike projections called cilia, whose synchronous beating propels the organisms. The characteristic example of free-living members of this group is *Paramecium caudatum*, and the parasitic example is *Balantidium coli*.

4. **Sporozoa:** Unlike other members of this phylum, sporozoa do not have locomotor organelles in their mature stage; however, immature forms exhibit some type of movement. All the members of this group are parasites. The most significant members belong to the genus *Plasmodium*, the malarial parasites of animals and humans.

Free-Living Protozoa

PURPOSE

To become familiar with the protozoan flora of pond water.

PRINCIPLE

There are more than 20,000 known species of free-living protozoa. It is not within the scope of this manual to present an in-depth study of this large and diverse population. Therefore in this procedure you will use Table 1 to become familiar with the general structural characteristics of representative protozoa, and you will identify these in a sample of pond water.

MATERIALS

Cultures

Stagnant pond water.

Reagent

Methyl cellulose.

Equipment

Microscope, glass slides, coverslips, and Pasteur pipettes.

PROCEDURE

1. Obtain a drop of pond water from the bottom of the culture and place it in the center of a clean slide.

2. Add a drop of methyl cellulose to the culture to slow down the movement of the protozoa.

3. Apply a coverslip in the following manner to prevent formation of air bubbles:

    a. Place one edge of the coverslip against the outer edge of the drop of culture.

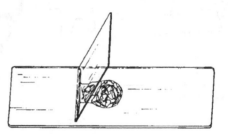

    b. After the drop of culture spreads along the inner aspect of the edge of the coverslip, gently lower the coverslip onto the slide.

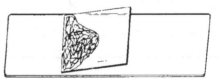

4. Examine your slide preparation under scanning, low-power, and high-power objectives with diminished light.

From *Microbiology: A Laboratory Manual*, Sixth Edition, James G. Cappuccino and Natalie Sherman. Copyright © 2002 Pearson Education, Inc., publishing as Benjamin Cummings. All rights reserved.

TABLE 1 Structural Characteristics of Free-Living Protozoa

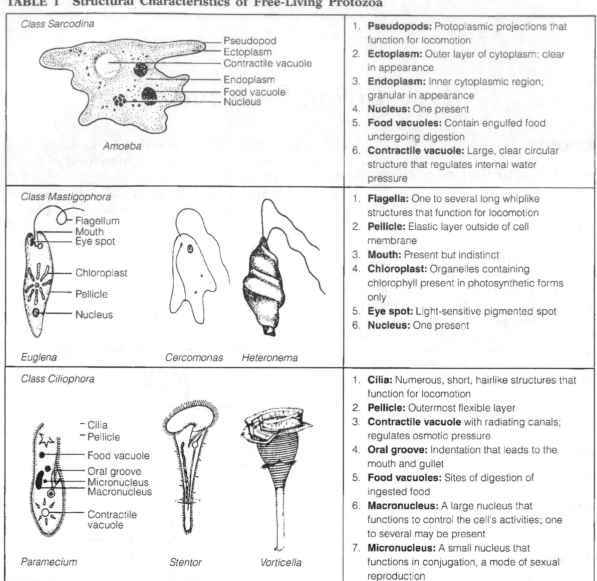

Class Sarcodina *Amoeba*	1. **Pseudopods:** Protoplasmic projections that function for locomotion 2. **Ectoplasm:** Outer layer of cytoplasm; clear in appearance 3. **Endoplasm:** Inner cytoplasmic region; granular in appearance 4. **Nucleus:** One present 5. **Food vacuoles:** Contain engulfed food undergoing digestion 6. **Contractile vacuole:** Large, clear circular structure that regulates internal water pressure
Class Mastigophora *Euglena Cercomonas Heteronema*	1. **Flagella:** One to several long whiplike structures that function for locomotion 2. **Pellicle:** Elastic layer outside of cell membrane 3. **Mouth:** Present but indistinct 4. **Chloroplast:** Organelles containing chlorophyll present in photosynthetic forms only 5. **Eye spot:** Light-sensitive pigmented spot 6. **Nucleus:** One present
Class Ciliophora *Paramecium Stentor Vorticella*	1. **Cilia:** Numerous, short, hairlike structures that function for locomotion 2. **Pellicle:** Outermost flexible layer 3. **Contractile vacuole** with radiating canals; regulates osmotic pressure 4. **Oral groove:** Indentation that leads to the mouth and gullet 5. **Food vacuoles:** Sites of digestion of ingested food 6. **Macronucleus:** A large nucleus that functions to control the cell's activities; one to several may be present 7. **Micronucleus:** A small nucleus that functions in conjugation, a mode of sexual reproduction

Free-Living Protozoa

Name   Section   Date

OBSERVATIONS AND RESULTS

1. Under the three objectives, observe your slide preparation for the different protozoa present.
2. In the space provided, draw a representative sketch of several of the observed protozoa, indicate the magnifications used, and label their structural components. Identify each organism according to its class based on its mode of locomotion and its genus.

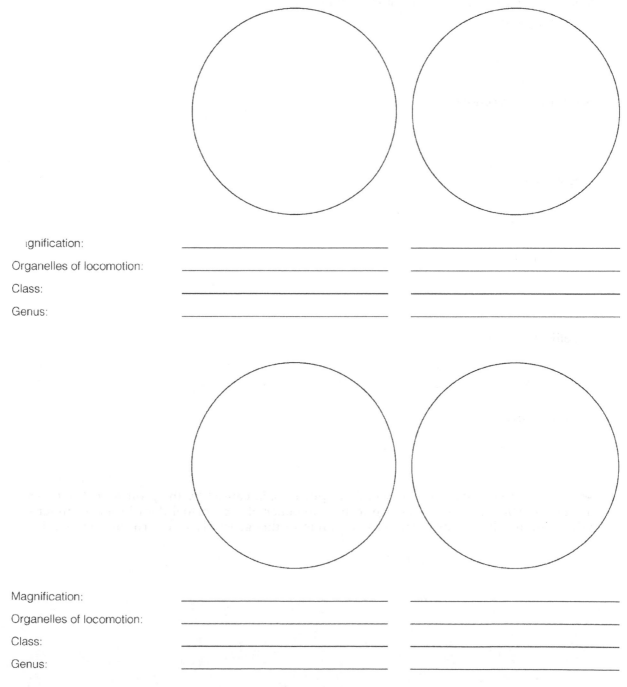

Magnification: _____ _____

Organelles of locomotion: _____ _____

Class: _____ _____

Genus: _____ _____

Magnification: _____ _____

Organelles of locomotion: _____ _____

Class: _____ _____

Genus: _____ _____

Free-Living Protozoa

REVIEW QUESTIONS

1. What are the distinguishing characteristics of the free-living members of Sarcodina, Mastigophora, and Ciliophora?

2. Identify and give the function of the following:
   a. Pseudopods:

   b. Contractile vacuole:

   c. Eye spot:

   d. Micronucleus:

   e. Pellicle:

   f. Oral groove:

3. People with AIDS are vulnerable to pneumonia caused by the protozoan *Pneumocystis carinii*. This organism is known to be a member of the normal flora in most humans. Why then are these individuals so susceptible to this generally rare form of pneumonia?

Phototrophs: Algae and Cyanobacteria

Objectives

After completing this exercise, you should be able to:

1. List criteria used to classify algae.
2. List general requirements for the growth of phototrophic organisms.
3. Compare and contrast algae with fungi and bacteria.

Background

Most freshwater phototrophs belong to the groups listed in Table 1. Of primary interest to microbiologists are the **cyanobacteria.** Cyanobacteria have prokaryotic cells and belong to the Domain Bacteria.

Algae is the common name for photosynthetic eukaryotic organisms that lack true roots, stems, and ˑes. Algae may be found in the ocean and in fresh-ˑr and on moist tree bark and soil. (See color plate IV.4.) Algae may be unicellular, colonial, filamentous, or multicellular. They exhibit a wide range of shapes: from the giant brown algae or kelp and delicate marine red algae to spherical green-algal colonies. Algae are classified according to pigments, storage products, the chemical composition of their cell walls, and flagella.

While the growth of phototrophs is essential in providing oxygen and food for other organisms, some filamentous algae, such as *Spirogyra*, are a nuisance to humans because they clog filters in water systems. Phototrophs can be used to determine the quality of water. Polluted waters containing excessive nutrients from sewage or other sources have more cyanobacteria and fewer diatoms than clean waters do. Additionally, the *number* of algal cells indicates water quality. More than 1,000 algal cells per milliliter indicates that excessive nutrients are present.

Materials

Pond water samples:

A. Incubated in the light for 4 weeks.
B. Incubated in the dark for 4 weeks.
C. With nitrates and phosphates added; incubated in the light for 4 weeks.
D. With copper sulfate added; incubated in the light for 4 weeks.

Table 1

Some Characteristics of Major Groups of Phototrophs Found in Freshwater

Characteristics	Bacteria	Algal Protists		
	Cyanobacteria	Euglenoids	Diatoms	Green Algae
Color	Blue-green	Green	Yellow-brown	Green
Cell wall	Bacteria-like	Lacking	Readily visible with regular markings	Visible
Cell type	Prokaryote	Eukaryote	Eukaryote	Eukaryote
Flagella	Absent	Present	Absent	Present in some
Cell arrangement	Unicellular or filamentous	Unicellular	Unicellular or colonial	Unicellular, colonial, or filamentous
Nutrition	Autotrophic	Facultatively heterotrophic	Autotrophic	Autotrophic
Produce O_2	Yes	Yes	Yes	Yes

From *Laboratory Experiments in Microbiology*, Sixth Edition, Ted R. Johnson and Christine L. Case.

Techniques Required

Compound light microscopy

Hanging drop

Procedure

1. Prepare a hanging-drop slide from a sample of pond water A. Take your drop from the bottom of the container. Why? _____
_____

2. Examine the slide using the low and high-dry objectives. Identify the algae present in the pond water. Draw those algae that you cannot identify. Record the relative amounts of each type of alga from 4+ (most abundant) to + (one representative seen).

3. Repeat the observation and data collection for the remaining pond water samples.

Phototrophs: Algae and Cyanobacteria

LABORATORY REPORT

Name _____

Date _____

Lab Section _____

Purpose _____

_____

_____

Data

Name of Alga or Cyanobacterium	Relative Abundance in Pond Water			
	Incubated in Light	Incubated in Dark	Incubated with NO_3^- and PO_4^{3-}	Incubated with $CuSO_4$
Drawings of other algae seen				
Total number of species				
Total number of organisms				

Which sample is the control? _____

Conclusions

Compare the number and various groups of algae observed in each environment with the control.

Dark vs. light (sample A)
In which sample did you expect more algae? _____

Why? _____

_____

_____

Did your findings agree with expected results? If not, briefly explain why. _____

_____

_____

Nitrate and phosphate vs. no nitrate and phosphate (sample A)
In which sample did you expect more algae? _____

Why? _____

_____

___   _____

Did your findings agree with expected results? If not, briefly explain why. _____

_____

_____

Copper vs. no copper (sample A)
In which sample did you expect more algae? _____

Why? _____

_____

_____

Did your findings agree with expected results? If not, briefly explain why. _____

_____

_____

Questions

1. Why can algae and cyanobacteria be considered indicators of productivity as well as of pollution? _____

_____

_____

2. How can algae be responsible for the production of more oxygen than land plants? _____

_____

_____

3. Why aren't algae included in the Kingdom Plantae? _____

_____

_____

_____

4. Describe one way in which algae and fungi differ. _____

_____

_____

How are they similar? _____

_____

_____

_____

Critical Thinking

1. Outbreaks of cyanobacterial intoxication associated with lakes and ponds are reported annually. What would cause an increased number of cases in summer months? Why aren't cyanobacterial intoxications associated with swimming pools?

2. Cyanobacteria were once called "blue-green algae." What characteristics would lead to the name "blue-green algae"? What caused biologists to reclassify them as cyanobacteria?

26

The Fungi

PURPOSES

1. To become familiar with the macroscopic and microscopic structure of yeasts and molds.
2. To become familiar with basic mycological culturing and staining procedures.
3. To provide an opportunity to identify a common fungal organism.

INTRODUCTION

The branch of microbiology that deals with the study of fungi (yeasts and molds) is called **mycology**. True fungi are separated into the following four classes on the basis of their sexual modes of reproduction:

1. **Phycomycetes:** Water, bread, and terrestrial molds. Reproductive spores are external and uncovered.
2. **Ascomycetes:** Yeasts and molds. Sexual spores, called ascospores, are produced in a saclike structure called an ascus.
3. **Basidiomycetes:** Fleshy fungi, toadstools, mushrooms, puffballs, and bracket fungi. Reproductive spores, basidiospores, are separate from specialized stalks called basidia.
4. **Deuteromycetes:** Also called **Fungi Imperfecti** because no sexual reproductive phase has been observed.

Nutritionally, the fungi are heterotrophic, eukaryotic microorganisms that are enzymatically capable of metabolizing a wide variety of organic substrates. Fungi can have beneficial or detrimental effects on humans. Those that inhabit the soil play a vital role in decomposing dead plant and animal tissues, thereby maintaining a fertile soil environment. The fermentative fungi are of industrial importance in producing beer and wine, bakery products, cheeses, industrial enzymes, and antibiotics. The detrimental activities of some fungi include spoilage of foods by rots, mildews, and rusts found on fruit, vegetables, and grains. Some species are capable of producing toxins (aflatoxin) and hallucinogens. A few fungal species are of medical significance because of their capacities to produce diseases in humans. Many of the pathogenic fungi are Deuteromycetes and can be divided into two groups based on site of infection. The **superficial mycoses** cause infections of the skin, hair, and nails (for example, ringworm infections). The **systemic mycoses** cause infections of the subcutaneous and deeper tissues such as those of the lungs, genital areas, and nervous system.

Blood Group Determination: Slide Agglutination

Objectives

After completing this exercise, you should be able to:

1. Compare and contrast the terms agglutination and hemagglutination.
2. Determine ABO and Rh blood types.
3. Determine possible compatible transfusions.

Background

Agglutination reactions occur between high-molecular-weight, particulate antigens and antibodies. Since many antigens are on cells, agglutination reactions lead to the clumping, or **agglutination,** of cells. When the involved are red blood cells, the reaction is called ...magglutination.

Hemagglutination reactions are used in the typing of blood. The presence or absence of two very similar carbohydrate antigens (designated A and B) located on the surface of red blood cells is determined using specific antisera (Figure 1). Hemagglutination occurs when anti-A antiserum is mixed with type A red blood cells. When anti-A antiserum is mixed with type B red blood cells, no hemagglutination occurs. People with type AB blood possess both A and B antigens on their red blood cells, and those with type O blood lack A and B antigens (see Figure 1).

Many other blood antigen series exist on human red blood cells. Another surface antigen on red blood cells is designated the Rh factor. The **Rh factor** is a complex of many antigens. The Rh factor that is used routinely in blood typing is the Rh_0 antigen, or **D antigen.** Individuals are Rh-positive when D antigen is present. The presence of the Rh factor is determined by a hemagglutination reaction between anti-D antiserum and red blood cells with D antigen on their surface.

A person possesses antibodies to the alternate antigen. Thus, people of blood type A will have antibodies to the B antigen in their sera (see Figure 1). Rh-negative individuals do not naturally have anti-D antibodies in their sera. Anti-D antibodies are produced when red blood cells with D antigen are introduced into Rh-negative individuals.

The ABO and Rh systems place restrictions on how blood may be transfused from one person to another. An incompatible transfusion results when the antigens of the donor red blood cells react with the antibodies in the recipient's serum or induce the formation of antibodies.

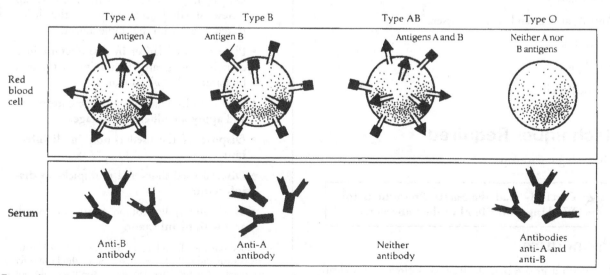

Figure 1

Relationship of antigens and antibodies involved in the ABO blood group system.

From *Laboratory Experiments in Microbiology,* Sixth Edition, Ted R. Johnson and Christine L. Case.

Table 1

The ABO and Rh Blood Group Systems

Characteristic	Blood Type					
	A	B	AB	O	Rh+	Rh–
Antigen present on the red blood cells	A	B	Both A and B	Neither A nor B	D	No D
Antibody normally present in the serum	Anti-B	Anti-A	Neither anti-A nor anti-B	Both anti-A and anti-B	No anti-D	No anti-D*
Serum causes agglutination of red blood cells of these types	B, AB	A, AB	None	A, B, AB	Neither Rh+ nor Rh–	Neither Rh+ nor Rh–*
Percent occurrence in a mixed Caucasian population	41	10	4	45	85	15
Percent occurrence in a mixed Black population	27	20	7	46	85	15

*Anti-D antibodies are not naturally present in the serum of Rhpeople. Anti-D antibodies can be produced upon exposure to the D antigen through blood transfusions or pregnancy.
Source: Adapted from G. J. Tortora, B. R. Funke, and C. L. Case. *Microbiology: An Introduction*, 7th ed. San Francisco, CA: Benjamin Cummings, 2001.

A s   ry of the major characteristics of the ABO and Rh blood groups is presented in Table 1.

Materials

Cotton moistened with 70% ethyl alcohol

Sterile cotton balls and bandage

Sterile lancet

Anti-A, anti-B, and anti-D antisera

Glass slides (2)

Toothpicks

Grease pencil

Techniques Required

Dissecting microscope

 Carefully read the Safety Precautions for Working with Blood in the Laboratory.

Procedure

1. With a grease pencil, draw two circles on a clean glass slide, and label one "A" and the other "B." Draw a circle on the second slide and label it "D."

Safety Precautions for Working with Blood in the Laboratory

- Do not perform this lab experiment if you are sick.
- Work only with **your own** blood* or wear gloves.
- **Disinfect** your finger with 70% alcohol. Use any finger except your thumb. Unwrap a **new, sterile** lancet and pierce the disinfected finger with the sterile lancet.
- Place the used lancet **in disinfectant** in a container designated by the instructor or a biohazard "sharps" container.
- Stop the bleeding with a sterile cotton ball and **apply an adhesive bandage.**
- **Dispose of** the used cotton **in disinfectant.**
- **Discard** used slides and toothpicks **in disinfectant.**
- **Wash** any spilled blood from your work area **with disinfectant.**

*Blood obtained from blood banks is tested for hepatitis B virus and HIV. However, no test method can offer complete assurance that laboratory specimens do not contain these viruses.

2. Disinfect your middle finger with cotton saturated in alcohol (Figure 2). Pierce the disinfected finger with a sterile lancet.

3. Let a drop of blood fall into each circle. Stop the bleeding with a sterile cotton ball, and apply an adhesive bandage.

4. To the A circle, add 1 drop of anti-A antiserum. Add 1 drop of anti-B antiserum to the B circle and 1 drop of anti-D antiserum to the D circle.

5. Mix each suspension with toothpicks. Use a different toothpick for each antiserum. Why? _____

_____

6. Observe for agglutination, and determine your blood type. A dissecting microscope may help you see hemagglutination.

> Discard the slides, toothpicks, cotton balls, and lancet in the disinfectant.

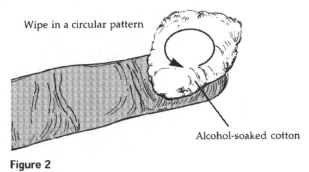

Wipe in a circular pattern

Alcohol-soaked cotton

Figure 2
To disinfect skin, rub it with 70% ethyl alcohol.

Blood Group Determination: Slide Agglutination

Name _____

Date _____

Lab Section _____

Purpose _____

_____

_____

Data

Antiserum	Hemagglutination
Anti-A	
ti-B	
Anti-D	

Data Analysis

On the blackboard, tabulate the blood types for the class or laboratory section. Calculate the percentage of each blood type, and compare with the percent distribution given in Table 1.

Blood Type	Number of Students	Percent
A		
B		
AB		
O		

Questions

1. What is your blood type? _____

2. What is the blood type of the person on your left? _____

Is your blood potentially compatible? _____ Explain briefly. _____

3. What is the blood type of the person on your right? _____

    Is your blood potentially compatible? _____ Explain briefly. _____

Critical Thinking

1. What is hemolytic disease of the newborn? How does Rhogam® prevent it?

2. How can blood type O be considered the "universal donor"?

3. Individuals have antibodies to the AB blood antigens not found on their red blood cells. What is the origin of these antibodies in someone who has never had a transfusion?

4. A woman with type A blood can have a healthy baby with type B blood. Why doesn't the baby develop hemolytic disease of the newborn?

Basic Laboratory Techniques for Isolation, Cultivation, and Cultural Characterization of Microorganisms

---
PURPOSES

To become familiar with

1. The types of laboratory equipment and culture media needed to develop and maintain pure cultures.
2. The concept of sterility and the procedures necessary for successful subculturing of microorganisms.
3. Streak-plate and spread-plate inoculations for separation of microorganisms in a mixed microbial population for subsequent pure culture isolation.
4. Cultural and morphological characteristics of microorganisms grown in pure culture.

INTRODUCTION

Microorganisms are ubiquitous. They are found in soil, air, water, food, sewage, and on body surfaces. In short, every area of our environment is replete with them. The microbiologist separates these mixed populations into individual species for study. A culture containing a single unadulterated species of cells is called a **pure culture**. To isolate and study microorganisms in pure culture, the microbiologist requires basic laboratory apparatus and the application of specific techniques, as illustrated in Figure 1.

Media

The survival and continued growth of microorganisms depend on an adequate supply of nutrients and a favorable growth environment. For the former, most microbes must use soluble low-molecular-weight substances that are frequently derived from the enzymatic degradation of complex nutrients. A solution containing these nutrients is a **culture medium**. Basically, all culture media are liquid, semisolid, or solid. A liquid medium lacks a solidifying agent and is called a **broth medium**. A broth medium supplemented with a solidifying agent called **agar** results in a solid or semisolid medium. Agar is an extract of seaweed, a complex carbohydrate composed mainly of galactose, and is without nutritional value. Agar serves as an excellent solidifying agent because it liquefies at 100°C and solidifies at 40°C. Because of these properties, organisms, especially pathogens,

36

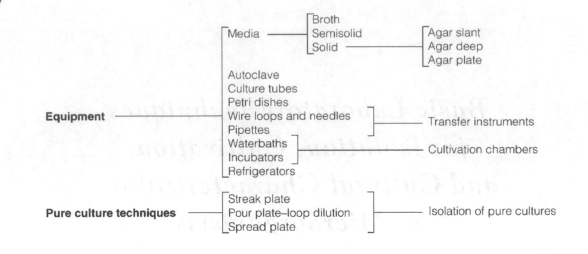

FIGURE 1   Laboratory apparatus and culture techniques

can be cultivated at temperatures of 37.5°C or slightly higher without fear of the medium liquefying. A completely solid medium requires an agar concentration of about 1.5 to 1.8%. A concentration of less than 1% agar results in a **semisolid medium**. A solid medium has the advantage that it presents a hardened surface on which microorganisms can be grown using specialized techniques for the isolation of discrete colonies. Each colony is a cluster of cells that originates from the multiplication of a single cell and represents the growth of a single species of microorganism. Such a defined and well-isolated colony is a **pure culture**. Also, while in the liquefied state, solid media can be placed in test tubes, which are then allowed to cool and harden in a slanted position, producing **agar slants**. These are useful for maintaining pure cultures. Similar tubes that, following preparation, are allowed to harden in the upright position are designated as **agar deep tubes**. Agar deep tubes are used primarily for the study of the gaseous requirements of microorganisms. However, they may be liquefied in a boiling water bath and poured into Petri dishes, producing **agar plates**, which provide large surface areas for the isolation and study of microorganisms. The various forms of solid media are illustrated in Figure 2.

In addition to nutritional needs, the environmental factors must also be regulated, including proper pH, temperature, gaseous requirements, and osmotic pressure.

Sterilization

Sterility is the hallmark of successful work in the microbiology laboratory. To achieve sterility, it is mandatory that you use sterile equipment and sterile techniques. **Sterilization** is the process of rendering a medium or material free of all forms of life. Figure 3 is a brief outline of the routine techniques used in the microbiology laboratory.

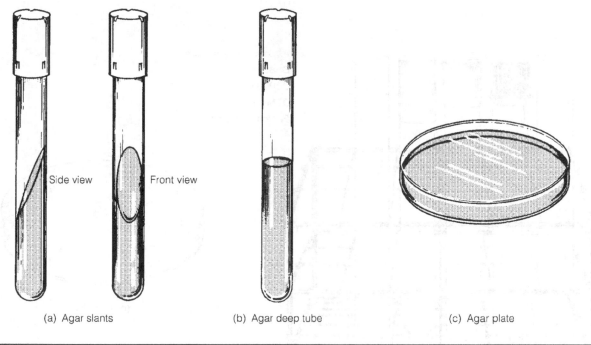

FIGURE 2 Forms of solid (agar) media

Culture Tubes and Petri Dishes

Glass **test tubes** and glass or plastic **Petri dishes** are used to cultivate microorganisms. A suitable nutrient medium in the form of
broth or agar may be added to the tubes, while only a solid medium
is used in Petri dishes. A sterile environment is maintained in

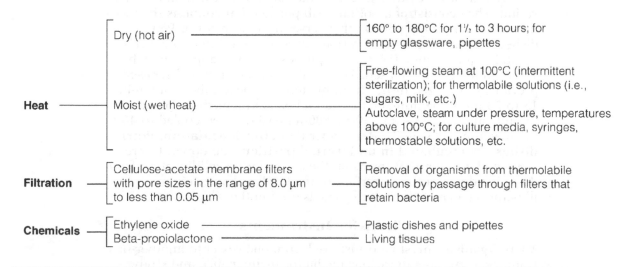

FIGURE 3 Sterilization techniques

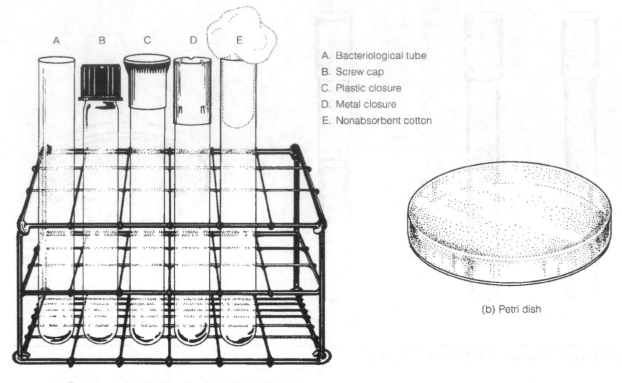

A. Bacteriological tube
B. Screw cap
C. Plastic closure
D. Metal closure
E. Nonabsorbent cotton

(b) Petri dish

(a) Test tube rack with tubes showing various closures

FIGURE 4 Culture vessels

culture tubes by various types of closures. Historically, the first type, a cotton plug, was developed by Schröeder and von Dusch in the nineteenth century. Today most laboratories use sleevelike caps made of metal, such as stainless steel, or heat-resistant plastics. The advantage of these closures over the cotton plug is that they are labor-saving and, most of all, slip on and off the test tubes easily.

Petri dishes provide a larger surface area for growth and cultivation. They consist of a bottom dish portion that contains the medium and a larger top portion that serves as a loose cover. Petri dishes are manufactured in various sizes to meet different experimental requirements. For routine purposes, dishes approximately 15 cm in diameter are used. The sterile agar medium is dispensed to previously sterilized dishes from molten agar deep tubes containing 15 to 20 ml of medium, or from a molten sterile medium prepared in bulk and contained in 250- to 500-ml flasks. When cooled to 40°C, the medium will solidify. Remember that **after inoculation, Petri dishes are incubated in an inverted position** (top down) to prevent condensation that forms on the cover during solidification from dropping down onto the surface of the hardened agar. Figure 4 illustrates some of the culture vessels used in the laboratory.

Transfer Instruments

Microorganisms must be transferred from one vessel to another or from stock cultures to various media for maintenance and study.

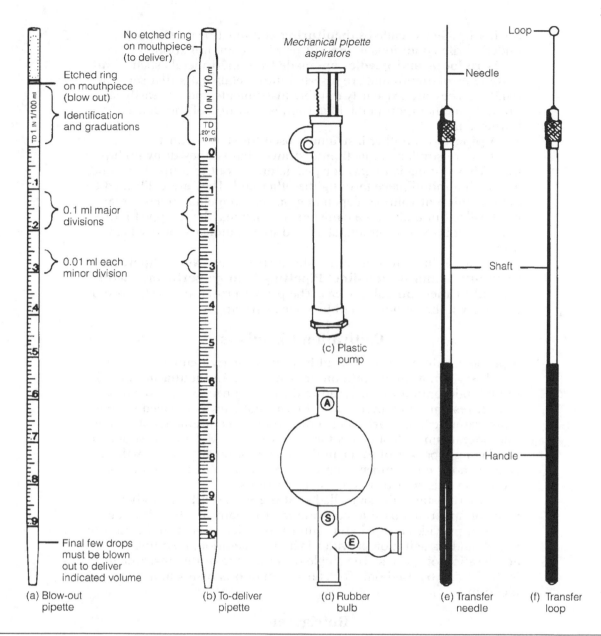

(a) Blow-out pipette

Etched ring on mouthpiece (blow out)

Identification and graduations

0.1 ml major divisions

0.01 ml each minor division

Final few drops must be blown out to deliver indicated volume

(b) To-deliver pipette

No etched ring on mouthpiece (to deliver)

Mechanical pipette aspirators

(c) Plastic pump

(d) Rubber bulb

Needle

Shaft

Handle

Loop

(e) Transfer needle

(f) Transfer loop

FIGURE 5   Transfer instruments

Basic Laboratory Techniques

Such a transfer is called **subculturing** and must be carried out under sterile conditions to prevent possible contamination.

Wire loops and needles are made from inert metals such as nichrome or platinum and are inserted into metal shafts that serve as handles. They are extremely durable instruments and are easily sterilized by incineration in the blue (hottest) portion of the Bunsen burner flame.

A **pipette** is another instrument used for sterile transfers. Pipettes are similar in function to straws; that is, they draw up liquids. They are made of glass or plastic drawn out to a tip at one end and with a mouthpiece forming the other end. They are calibrated to deliver different volumes depending on requirements. Pipettes may be sterilized in bulk inside canisters, or they may be wrapped individually in brown paper and sterilized in an autoclave or dry-heat oven.

Figure 5 illustrates these transfer instruments. **Note: Pipetting by mouth is not permissible! Pipetting is to be performed with the aid of mechanical devices.** The proper procedure for the use of pipettes will be demonstrated by your instructor.

Cultivation Chambers

A prime requirement for the cultivation of microorganisms is that they be grown at their optimum temperature. An **incubator** is used to maintain optimum temperature during the necessary growth period. It resembles an oven and is thermostatically controlled so that temperature can be varied depending on the requirements of specific microorganisms. Most incubators use dry heat. Moisture is supplied by placing a beaker of water in the incubator during the growth period. A moist environment retards dehydration of the medium and thereby avoids spurious experimental results.

A thermostatically controlled **shaking waterbath** is another piece of apparatus used to cultivate microorganisms. Its advantage is that it provides a rapid and uniform transfer of heat to the culture vessel, and its agitation provides increased aeration, resulting in acceleration of growth. The single disadvantage of this instrument is that it can be used only for cultivation of organisms in a broth medium.

Refrigerator

A refrigerator is used for a wide variety of purposes such as maintenance and storage of stock cultures between subculturing periods and storage of sterile media to prevent dehydration. It is also used as a repository for thermolabile solutions, antibiotics, serums, and biochemical reagents.

Microbes in the Environment

Whatever is worth doing at all
is worth doing well.

PHILIP DORMER STANHOPE

Objectives

After completing this exercise, you should be able to:

1. Describe colony morphology using accepted descriptive terms.
2. Compare bacterial growth on solid and liquid culture media.
3. Describe why agar is used in culture media.
4. Prepare nutrient broth and nutrient agar.

Background

...robes are everywhere; they are found in the water we drink, the air we breathe, and the earth we walk on. They live in and on our bodies. Microbes occupy ecological niches on all forms of life and in most environments. In most situations, the ubiquitous microorganisms are harmless. However, in microbiology, work must be done carefully to avoid contaminating sterile media and materials with these microbes.

In this exercise, we will attempt to culture (grow) some microbes. When a medium is selected for culturing bacteria, macronutrients, an energy source, and any necessary growth factors must be provided. A medium whose exact chemical composition is known is called a **chemically defined medium** (Table 1).

Most chemoheterotrophic bacteria are routinely grown on **complex media**—that is, media for which the exact chemical composition varies slightly from batch to batch. Organic carbon, energy, and nitrogen sources are usually supplied by protein in the form of meat extracts and partially digested proteins called *peptones*. **Nutrient broth** is a commonly used liquid complex medium. When agar is added, it becomes a solid medium, called **nutrient agar** (Table 2).

Agar, an extract from marine red algae, has some unique properties that make it useful in culture media. Few microbes can degrade agar, so it remains solid during microbial growth. It liquefies at 100°C and remains in a liquid state until cooled to 40°C. Once the agar has solidified, it can be incubated at temperatures up to 100°C and remain solid.

Table 1
Glucose–Minimal Salts Broth

Ingredient	Amount/100 ml
Glucose	0.5 g
Sodium chloride (NaCl)	0.5 g
Ammonium dihydrogen phosphate ($NH_4H_2PO_4$)	0.1 g
Dipotassium phosphate (K_2HPO_4)	0.1 g
Magnesium sulfate ($MgSO_4$)	0.02 g
Distilled water	100 ml

Table 2
Nutrient Agar

Ingredient	Amount/100 ml
Peptone	0.5 g
Beef extract	0.3 g
Sodium chloride (NaCl)	0.8 g
Agar	1.5 g
Distilled water	100 ml

Media must be sterilized after preparation. The most common method of sterilizing culture media that are heat stable is **steam sterilization,** or **autoclaving,** using steam under pressure. During this process, material to be sterilized is placed in the autoclave and heated to 121°C at 15 pounds of pressure (15 psi) for 15 minutes.

Culture media can be prepared in various forms, depending on the desired use. **Petri plates** containing solid media provide a large surface area for examination of colonies. The microbes will be **inoculated,** or intentionally introduced, onto nutrient agar and into nutrient broth. The bacteria that are inoculated into culture media increase in number during an **incubation period.** After suitable incubation, liquid media become **turbid,** or cloudy, due to bacterial growth. On solid media, colonies will be visible to the naked eye. A **colony** is a population of cells that arises from a single bacterial cell. A colony may arise from a group of the same microbes attached to one another, which is therefore called a **colony-forming unit.** Although many species of bacteria give rise to colonies that appear similar, each colony that appears different is usually a different species.

Materials

250 ml Erlenmeyer flask with cap or plug

100 ml graduated cylinder

Distilled water

Nutrient broth powder

Agar

Glass stirring rod

5 ml ρ

Test tubes with caps (2)

Sterile Petri dishes (4)

Balance

Weighing paper or dish

Autoclave gloves

Hot plate

Tube containing sterile cotton swabs

Tube containing sterile water

Demonstration

Use of the autoclave

Techniques Required

Pipetting

Procedure

First Period

A. Preparation of culture media

1. Prepare 100 ml of nutrient broth in a 250 ml flask. Using the graduated cylinder, add 100 ml of distilled water to the flask. Read the preparation instructions on the nutrient broth bottle. Calculate the amount of nutrient broth powder needed for 100 ml. If the amount needed for 1000 ml is _____ grams, then _____ grams are needed for 100 ml. Weigh out the required amount and add it to the flask. Stir with a glass rod until the powder is dissolved.

2. Pipette 5 ml of the nutrient broth into each test tube and cap each tube. Label the tubes "nutrient broth." Place one in the To Be Autoclaved rack. Label the remaining tube "not sterile," and incubate it at room temperature until the next period.

3. Add agar (1.5% w/v) to the remaining 90 ml of nutrient broth. What quantity of agar will you need to add? _____

4. Bring the broth to a boil and continue boiling carefully until all the agar is dissolved. *Be careful:* Do not let the solution boil over. Stir often to prevent burning and boiling over.

5. Stopper the flask, label it "nutrient agar," and place the flask and tube in the To Be Autoclaved basket.

6. The instructor will demonstrate use of the autoclave.

7. After autoclaving, allow the flasks and tube to cool to room temperature, or proceed to part B. What effect does the agar have on the culture medium? _____

B. Pouring plates

Transfer the melted sterile nutrient agar flasks to a 45°C water bath. Allow the flask of nutrient agar to cool to about 45°C (warm to the touch). If the agar has solidified, it will have to be reheated to liquefy it. To what temperature will it have to be heated?

_____

The sterile nutrient agar must be poured into Petri plates *aseptically*—that is, without letting microbes into the nutrient medium. *Read the following procedure before beginning* so that you can work quickly and efficiently.

1. Set four sterile, unopened Petri plates in front of you with the cover (larger half) on top. Have a lighted laboratory burner within reach on your workbench.

> **Keep the burner away from your hair and in the center of the bench.**

2. Holding the flask at an angle, remove the stopper with the fourth and fifth fingers of your other hand. Heat the mouth of the flask by passing it briefly through the flame (Figure 1a). Why is it necessary to keep the flask at an angle through this procedure? _____

_____

3. Remove the cover from the first plate with the hand holding the plug. Quickly and neatly pour melted nutrient agar into the plate until the bot-

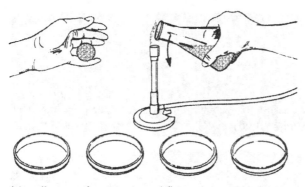

(a) Remove the stopper, and flame the mouth of the flask.

(b) Remove the cover from one plate, and pour nutrient agar into the plate bottom.

figure 1
Petri plate pouring.

tom is just covered to a depth of approximately 5 mm (Figure 1b). Keep the flask at an angle, and replace the plate cover; move on to the next plate until all the agar is poured.

4. When all the agar is poured, gently swirl the agar in each plate to cover any empty spaces; do not allow the agar to touch the sides or covers of the plates.

5. To decrease condensation, leave the Petri plate covers slightly ajar for about 15 minutes until the agar solidifies.

6. Place the empty flask in the discard area.

C. Culturing microbes from the environment

1. Design your own experiment. The purpose is to sample your environment and your body. Use your imagination. Here are some suggestions:
   a. You may use the lab, a washroom, or any place on campus for the environment.
   b. One nutrient agar plate might be left open to the air for 30 to 60 minutes.

c. Inoculate a plate from an environmental surface such as the floor or workbench by wetting a cotton swab in sterile water, swabbing the environmental surface, and then swabbing the surface of the agar. Why is the swab first moistened in sterile water? _____

   _____

   After inoculation, the swab should be discarded in the container of disinfectant.

2. Inoculate two plates from the environment. Inoculate one nutrient broth tube using a swab as described in step 1c. After swabbing the agar surface, place the swab in the nutrient broth and leave it there during incubation. You may need to break off part of the wooden handle to fit the swab into the nutrient broth.

3. The plates and tube should be incubated at the approximate temperature of the environment sampled.

4. Inoculate two plates from your body. You could:
   a. Place a hair on the agar.
   b. Obtain an inoculum by swabbing (see step 1c) part of your body with a wet swab.
   c. Touch the plate with your fingers.

5. Incubate bacteria from your body at or close to your body temperature. What is human body temperature? _____ °C

6. Incubate all plates inverted, so water will condense in the lid instead of on the surface of the agar. Why is condensation on the agar undesirable?

   _____

   _____

7. Incubate all inoculated media until the next laboratory period.

Second Period

1. Observe and describe the resulting growth on the plates. Note each different-appearing colony, and describe the colony morphology using the characteristics given in Figure 2. Determine the approximate number of each type of colony. When many colonies are present, record TNTC (too numerous to count) as the number of colonies.

2. Describe the appearance of the nutrient broth labeled "not sterile" and the broth you inoculated. Are they uniformly cloudy or turbid? Look for clumps of microbial cells, called **flocculant.** Is there a membrane, or **pellicle,** across the surface of the broth? See whether microbial cells have settled on the bottom of the tube, forming a **sediment.**

3. Discard the plates and tubes properly.

> **Place contaminated plates in the biohazard bag for autoclaving.**

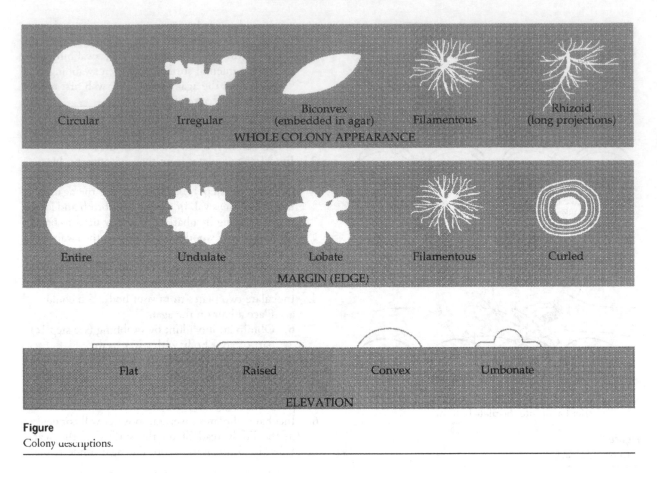

Figure
Colony descriptions.

Microbes in the Environment

LABORATORY REPORT

Name _____

Date _____

Lab Section _____

Purpose _____
_____
_____

Data

Fill in the following table with descriptions of the bacterial colonies. Use a separate line for each different-appearing colony.

	Colony Description					
	Diameter	Appearance	Margin	Elevation	Color	Number of This Type
Area sampled: _____ Incubated at _____ °C for _____ days						
Area sampled: _____ Incubated at _____ °C for _____ days						
Area sampled: _____ Incubated at _____ °C for _____ days						

	Colony Description					
	Diameter	Appearance	Margin	Elevation	Color	Number of This Type
Area sampled:						
_____						
Incubated at						
_____ °C for						
_____ days						

Nutrient broths: Incubated at _____ °C for _____ days

	Unsterile Broth	Inculated Broth Area Sampled: _____
Turbidity		
Flocculant present		
Sediment present		
Pellicle present		
Color		

Questions

1. What observations can you make about the variety and number of colonies observed on the different plates? (For example, did one environment have more bacteria? Why?) _____

   _____

2. How can you tell whether or not there is bacterial growth in nutrient broth? _____

   _____

3. What is the minimum number of different bacteria present on one of your plates? _____

   How do you know? _____

   _____

4. What physical and chemical properties of agar make it useful in culture media? _____

   _____

   _____

5. What is the value of Petri plates in microbiology? _____

_____

Critical Thinking

1. Did all the organisms living in or on the environments sampled grow on your nutrient agar? Briefly explain.

2. How could you determine whether the turbidity in your nutrient broth tube was from a mixture of different microbes or from the growth of only one kind of microbe?

48

Cultural Characteristics
of Microorganisms

PURPOSE

To determine the cultural characteristics of microorganisms as an aid in identifying and classifying organisms into taxonomic groups.

PRINCIPLE

When grown on a variety of media, microorganisms will exhibit differences in the macroscopic appearance of their growth. These differences, called **cultural characteristics**, are used as the basis for separating microorganisms into taxonomic groups. The cultural characteristics for all known microorganisms are contained in *Bergey's Manual Systematic Bacteriology*. They are determined by culturing the organisms on nutrient agar slants and plates, in nutrient broth, and in nutrient gelatin. The patterns of growth to be considered in each of these media are described below, and some are illustrated in Figure 1.

Nutrient Agar Slants

These have a single straight line of inoculation on the surface and are evaluated in the following manner:

1. **Abundance of growth:** The amount of growth is designated as none, slight, moderate, or large.
2. **Pigmentation:** Chromogenic microorganisms may produce intracellular pigments that are responsible for the coloration of the organisms as seen in surface colonies. Other organisms produce extracellular soluble pigments that are excreted into the medium and that also produce a color. Most organisms, however, are nonchromogenic and will appear white to gray.

3. **Optical characteristics:** Optical characteristics may be evaluated on the basis of the amount of light transmitted through the growth. These characteristics are described as **opaque** (no light transmission), **translucent** (partial transmission), or **transparent** (full transmission).
4. **Form:** The appearance of the single-line streak of growth on the agar surface is designated as:
   a. **Filiform:** Continuous, threadlike growth with smooth edges.
   b. **Echinulate:** Continuous, threadlike growth with irregular edges.
   c. **Beaded:** Nonconfluent to semiconfluent colonies.
   d. **Effuse:** Thin, spreading growth.
   e. **Arborescent:** Treelike growth.
   f. **Rhizoid:** Rootlike growth.

Nutrient Agar Plates

These demonstrate well-isolated colonies and are evaluated in the following manner:

1. **Size:** Pinpoint, small, moderate, or large.
2. **Pigmentation:** Color of colony.
3. **Form:** The shape of the colony is described as follows:
   a. **Circular:** Unbroken, peripheral edge.
   b. **Irregular:** Indented, peripheral edge.
   c. **Rhizoid:** Rootlike, spreading growth.
4. **Margin:** The appearance of the outer edge of the colony is described as follows:
   a. **Entire:** Sharply defined, even.
   b. **Lobate:** Marked indentations.
   c. **Undulate:** Wavy indentations.
   d. **Serrate:** Toothlike appearance.
   e. **Filamentous:** Threadlike, spreading edge.

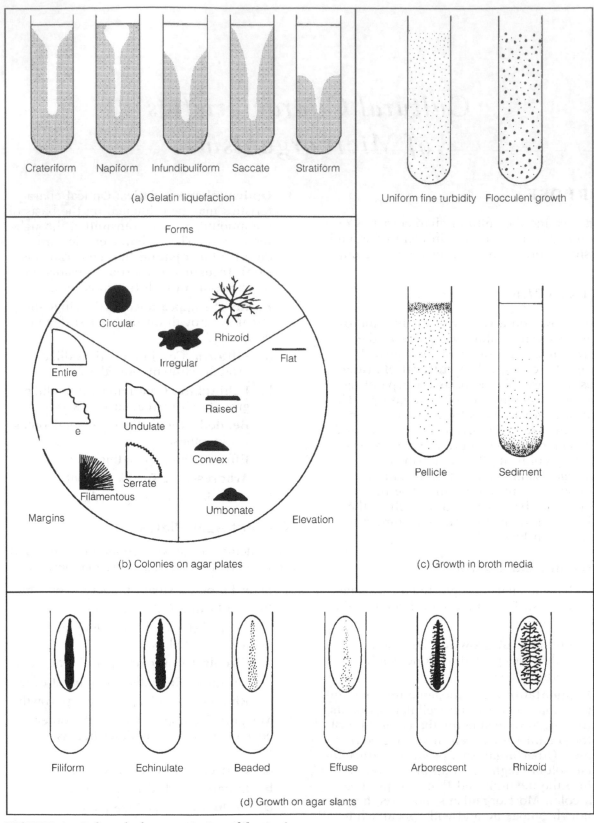

FIGURE 1 Cultural characteristics of bacteria

5. **Elevation:** The degree to which colony growth is raised on the agar surface is described as follows:
   a. **Flat:** Elevation not discernible.
   b. **Raised:** Slightly elevated.
   c. **Convex:** Dome-shaped elevation.
   d. **Umbonate:** Raised, with elevated convex central region.

Nutrient Broth Cultures

These are evaluated as to the distribution and appearance of the growth as follows:

1. **Uniform fine turbidity:** Finely dispersed growth throughout.
2. **Flocculent:** Flaky aggregates dispersed throughout.
3. **Pellicle:** Thick, padlike growth on surface.
4. **Sediment:** Concentration of growth at the bottom of broth culture may be granular, flaky, or flocculant.

Nutrient Gelatin

This solid medium may be liquefied by the zymatic action of gelatinase. Liquefaction curs in a variety of patterns:

1. **Crateriform:** Liquefied surface area is saucer-shaped.
2. **Napiform:** Bulbous-shaped liquefaction at surface.
3. **Infundibuliform:** Funnel-shaped.
4. **Saccate:** Elongated, tubular.
5. **Stratiform:** Complete liquefaction of the upper half of the medium.

MATERIALS

Cultures

24-hour nutrient broth cultures of *Pseudomonas aeruginosa*, *Bacillus cereus*, *Micrococcus luteus*, *Escherichia coli*, and *Staphylococcus aureus*.

Media

Per designated student group: five each of nutrient agar plates, nutrient agar slants, nutrient broth tubes, and nutrient gelatin tubes.

Equipment

Bunsen burner, inoculating loop and needle, and glassware marking pencil.

PROCEDURE

1. Using sterile technique, inoculate each of the appropriately labeled media listed below in the following manner:
   a. Nutrient agar plates: With a sterile loop, prepare a streak-plate inoculation of each of the cultures for the isolation of discrete colonies.
   b. Nutrient agar slants: With a sterile needle, make a single-line streak of each of the cultures provided, starting at the butt and drawing the needle up the center of the slanted agar surface.
   c. Nutrient broth: Using a sterile loop, inoculate each organism into a tube of nutrient broth. Shake the loop a few times to dislodge the inoculum.
   d. Nutrient gelatin: Using a sterile needle, prepare a stab inoculation of each of the cultures provided.
2. Incubate all cultures at 37°C for 24 to 48 hours.

Name   Section   Date

OBSERVATIONS AND RESULTS

Refer to Figure 1 and the descriptions presented in the introductory section while making the following observations:

1. Place all gelatin cultures in a refrigerator for 30 minutes to determine whether liquefaction of the medium has developed. Record your observations in the chart below according to the presence or absence of liquefaction and its type (if it has occurred).

Nutrient Gelatin Cultures					
	M. luteus	P. aeruginosa	S. aureus	E. coli	B. cereus
Draw liquefaction patterns.					
Liquefaction (+) or (−) Type of liquefaction					

2. Observe a single, well-isolated colony on each of the nutrient agar plate cultures and identify its size, elevation, margin, consistency, and pigmentation. Record your observations in the chart below.

Nutrient Agar Plates					
	M. luteus	P. aeruginosa	S. aureus	E. coli	B. cereus
Draw distribution of colonies.					
Size Elevation Margin Consistency Pigmentation					

Cultural Characteristics of Microorganisms

54

3. Observe each of the nutrient agar slant cultures for the amount, pigmentation, consistency, and form of the growth. Record your observations in the chart below.

Nutrient Agar Slant Cultures					
	M. luteus	*P. aeruginosa*	*S. aureus*	*E. coli*	*B. cereus*
Draw the distribution of growth on slant surface.					
Amount of growth					
Pigmentation					
Consistency					
Form					

4. Ol ⋅ each of the nutrient broth cultures for the appearance of the growth (flocculation, tu y, sediment, or pellicle). Record your results in the chart below.

Nutrient Broth Cultures					
	M. luteus	*P. aeruginosa*	*S. aureus*	*E. coli*	*B. cereus*
Draw the distribution of growth.					
Appearance of growth					

Cultural Characteristics of Microorganisms

Transfer of Bacteria: Aseptic Technique

Study without thinking is worthless; thinking without study is dangerous.

CONFUCIUS

Objectives

After completing this exercise, you should be able to:

1. Provide the rationale for aseptic technique.
2. Differentiate among the following: broth culture, agar slant, and agar deep.
3. Aseptically transfer bacteria from one form of culture medium to another.

Background

In the laboratory, bacteria must be cultured in order to facilitate identification and to examine their growth and metabolism. Bacteria are **inoculated,** or introduced, into various forms of culture media in order to keep them alive and to study their growth. Inoculations must be done without introducing unwanted microbes, or **contaminants,** into the media. **Aseptic technique** is used in microbiology to exclude contaminants.

All culture media are **sterilized,** or rendered free of all life, prior to use. Sterilization is usually accomplished using an autoclave. Containers of culture media, such as test tubes or Petri plates, should not be opened until you are ready to work with them, and even then, they should not be left open.

Broth cultures provide large numbers of bacteria in a small space and are easily transported. **Agar slants** are test tubes containing solid culture media that were left at an angle while the agar solidified. Agar slants, like Petri plates, provide a solid growth surface, but slants care eas-

ier to store and transport than Petri plates. Agar is allowed to solidify in the bottom of a test tube to make an **agar deep.** Deeps are often used to grow bacteria that prefer less oxygen than is present on the surface of the medium. Semisolid agar deeps containing 0.5–0.7% agar instead of the usual 1.5% agar can be used to determine whether a bacterium is motile. Motile bacteria will move away from the point of inoculation, giving the appearance of an inverted Christmas tree.

Transfer and inoculation are usually performed with a sterile, heat-resistant, noncorroding Nichrome wire attached to an insulated handle. When the end of the wire is bent into a loop, it is called an **inoculating loop;** when straight, it is an **inoculating needle** (Figure 1). For special purposes, cultures may also be transferred with sterile cotton swabs, pipettes, glass rods, or syringes. These techniques will be introduced in later exercises.

Whether to use an inoculating loop or a needle depends on the form of the medium; after completing this exercise, you will be able to decide which instrument is to be used.

Materials

Tubes containing nutrient broth (3)

Tubes containing nutrient agar slants (3)

Tubes containing nutrient semisolid agar deeps (3)

Inoculating loop

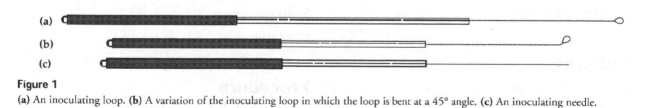

Figure 1

(a) An inoculating loop. **(b)** A variation of the inoculating loop in which the loop is bent at a 45° angle. **(c)** An inoculating needle.

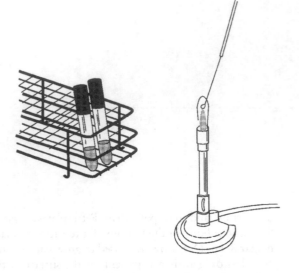

(a) Sterilize the loop by holding the wire in the flame until it is red hot.

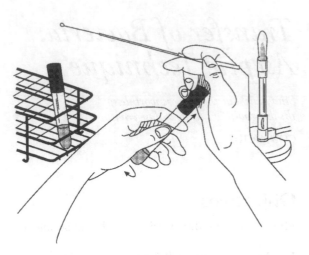

(b) While holding the sterile loop and the bacterial culture, remove the cap as shown.

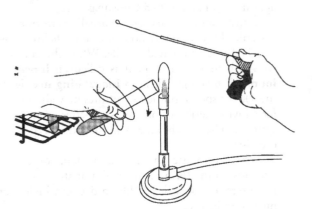

(c) Briefly heat the mouth of the tube in the flame before inserting the loop for an inoculum.

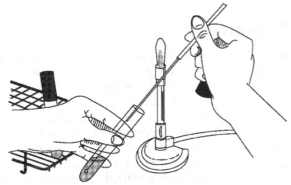

(d) Get a loopful of culture, heat the mouth of the tube, and replace the cap.

Figure 2
Inoculating procedures.

Inoculating needle

Test tube rack

Gram staining reagents

Cultures

Lactococcus lactis broth

Pseudomonas aeruginosa broth

Proteus vulgaris slant

Techniques Required

Compound light microscopy

Smear preparation

Gram staining

Procedure

1. Work with only one of the bacterial cultures at a time, to prevent any mix-ups or cross-contamination.

Label one tube of each media with the name of the first culture, your name, the date, and your lab section. Inoculate each tube as described and then work with the next culture. Begin with one of the broth cultures, and gently tap the bottom of it to resuspend the sediment.

2. To inoculate nutrient broth, hold the inoculating loop in your dominant hand and one of the broth cultures of bacteria in the other hand.

   a. Sterilize the loop by holding the wire in a Bunsen burner flame (Figure 2a). Heat to redness. Why? _____

   b. Holding the loop like a pencil or paintbrush, curl the little finger of the same hand around the cap of the broth culture. Gently pull the cap off the tube while turning the culture tube (Figure 2b). If cotton stoppers are used, simply grasp the stopper with your finger. Do not set the cap down. Why not? _____

   c. Holding the tube at an angle, pass the mouth of the tube through the flame (Figure 2c). What is the purpose of flaming the mouth of the tube?

   _____

   Always hold culture tubes and uninoculated tubes at an angle to minimize the amount of dust that could fall into them. Do not tip the tube too far, or the liquid will leak out around the loose-fitting cap.

   d. Immerse the sterilized, cooled loop into the broth culture to obtain a loopful of culture (Figure 2d). Why must the loop be cooled first? _____
   Remove the loop, and while holding the loop, flame the mouth of the tube and recap it by turning the tube into the cap. Place the tube in your test tube rack.

   e. Remove the cap from a tube of sterile nutrient broth as previously described, and flame the mouth of the tube. Immerse the inoculating loop into the sterile broth and then withdraw it from the tube. Flame the mouth of the tube and replace the cap. Return the tube to the test tube rack.

   f. Reflame the loop until it is red and let it cool. Some prefer to hold several tubes in their hands at once (Figure 3). *Do not* attempt holding and transferring between multiple tubes until you have mastered aseptic transfer techniques.

3. Obtain a nutrient agar slant. Repeat steps 2a–2d, and inoculate the slant by moving the loop gently across the agar surface from the bottom of the slant to the top, being careful not to gouge the agar (Figure 4). Flame the mouth of the tube and replace the cap. Flame your loop and let it cool.

4. Obtain a nutrient semisolid agar deep, and using your inoculating *needle*, repeat steps 2a–2d. Inocu-

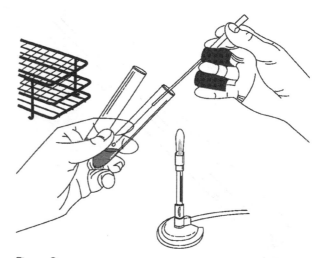

Figure 3

Experienced laboratory technicians can transfer cultures aseptically while holding multiple test tubes.

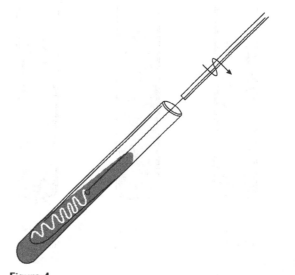

Figure 4

Inoculate a slant by streaking the loop back and forth across the surface of the agar.

late the semisolid agar deep by plunging the needle straight down the middle of the deep then pulling it out through the same stab, as shown in Figure 5. Flame the mouth of the tube and replace the cap. Flame your needle and let it cool.

5. Using the other broth culture, label one tube of each media as described in step 1; and inoculate a broth culture, agar slant, and semisolid agar deep, as described in steps 2, 3, and 4, using your inoculating *needle*.

6. Label one tube of each media with *Proteus vulgaris* as described in step 1. To transfer *Proteus vulgaris*, flame your loop and allow it to cool. Flame the mouth of the tube, and use your inoculating loop

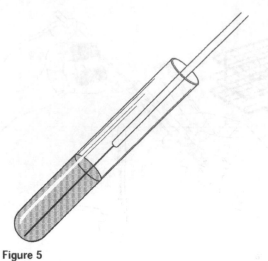

to carefully scrape a small amount of the culture from the agar. Flame the mouth of the tube and replace the cap. Inoculate a broth and a slant as described in steps 2 and 3. Inoculate a semisolid agar deep with an inoculating needle as described in step 4.

7. Incubate all tubes at 35°C until the next period.
8. Record the appearance of each culture, referring to Figure 6.
9. Make a smear of the *Lactococcus* broth culture and the *Lactococcus* slant culture. Gram stain both smears and compare them.

Figure 5
Inoculate an agar deep by stabbing into the agar with a needle.

| Arborescent (branched) | Beaded | Echinulate (pointed) | Filiform (even) | Rhizoid (rootlike) | Spreading |

Figure 6
Patterns of growth on agar slants.

Transfer of Bacteria: Aseptic Technique

LABORATORY REPORT

Name _____

Date _____

Lab Section _____

Purpose _____

_____

_____

Data

Nutrient Broth

Describe the nutrient broth cultures.

Bacterium	Is it turbid?	Is flocculant, pellicle, or sediment present?	Pigment
ctococcus lactis			
Pseudomonas aeruginosa			
Proteus vulgaris			

Nutrient Agar Slant

Sketch the appearance of each culture. Note any pigmentation.

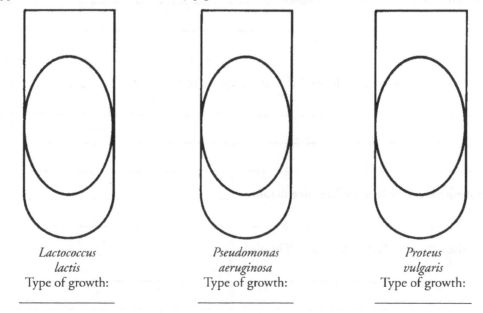

Lactococcus lactis
Type of growth:
_____

Pseudomonas aeruginosa
Type of growth:
_____

Proteus vulgaris
Type of growth:
_____

Nutrient Semisolid Agar Deep

Show the location of bacterial growth and note any pigment formation.

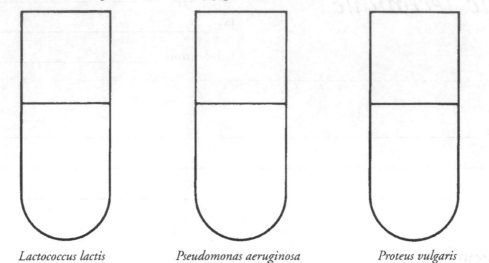

| *Lactococcus lactis* | *Pseudomonas aeruginosa* | *Proteus vulgaris* |

Comparison of Broth and Slant Cultures

	Lactococcus lactis	
	Broth Culture	Slant Culture
Gram		
Morphology		
Arrangement		

Questions

1. Did growth occur at different levels in the agar deep? _____

_____

_____

2. Were any of the bacteria growing in the semisolid agar deeps motile? Explain. _____

_____

_____

_____

3. What other methods can be used to determine motility? _____

_____

4. What is the primary use of slants? Of deeps? Of broths? _____

_____

_____

5. Can you determine whether a broth culture is pure (all one species) by visually inspecting it without a micro-

scope? _____ An agar deep culture? _____

An agar slant culture? _____

6. When is a loop preferable for transferring bacteria? Use an illustration from your results to answer. When is a

needle preferable? _____

_____

_____

7. What is the purpose of flaming the loop before use? After use? _____

_____

_____

8. Why must the loop be cool before touching it to a culture? Should you set it down to let it cool? How do you

determine when it is cool? _____

_____

_____

9. Why is aseptic technique important? _____

_____

_____

Critical Thinking

1. Why was the arrangement of *Lactococcus* from the broth culture different than that from the slant culture in the second period?

2. What evolutionary advantage would there be to the formation of a pellicle in a liquid medium by a bacterium?

3. How can you tell that the media provided for this exercise were sterile?

7

Techniques for Isolation of Pure Cultures

In nature, microbial populations do not segregate themselves by species but exist with a mixture of many other cell types. In the laboratory, these populations can be separated into **pure cultures**. These cultures contain only one type of organism and are suitable for the study of their cultural, morphological, and biochemical properties.

In this experiment, you will first use one of the techniques designed to produce discrete colonies. Colonies are individual, macroscopically visible masses of microbial growth on a solid medium surface, each representing the multiplication of a single organism. Once you have obtained these discrete colonies, you will make an aseptic transfer onto nutrient agar slants for the isolation of pure cultures.

PART A: Isolation of Discrete Colonies from a Mixed Culture

PURPOSE

To perform the spread-plate and/or the streak-plate inoculation procedure for the separation of the cells of a mixed culture so that discrete colonies can be isolated.

PRINCIPLE

The techniques commonly used for isolation of discrete colonies initially require that the number of organisms in the inoculum be reduced. The resulting diminution of the population size ensures that, following inoculation, individual cells will be sufficiently far apart on the surface of the agar medium to effect a separation of the different species present. The following are techniques that can be used to accomplish this necessary dilution:

1. The **streak-plate** method is a rapid qualitative isolation method. It is essentially a

dilution technique that involves spreading a loopful of culture over the surface of an agar plate. Although many types of procedures are performed, the four-way, or quadrant, streak is described. Refer to Figure 1, which schematically illustrates this procedure.

a. Place a loopful of culture on the agar surface in Area 1. Flame and cool the loop, then drag it rapidly several times across the surface of Area 1.

b. Reflame and cool the loop, and turn the Petri dish 90°. Then touch the loop to a corner of the culture in Area 1 and drag it several times across the agar in Area 2. The loop should never enter Area 1 again.

c. Reflame and cool the loop and again turn the dish 90°. Streak Area 3 in the same manner as Area 2.

d. Without reflaming the loop, again turn the dish 90° and then drag the culture from a corner of Area 3 across Area 4, using a wider streak. Don't let the loop touch any of the

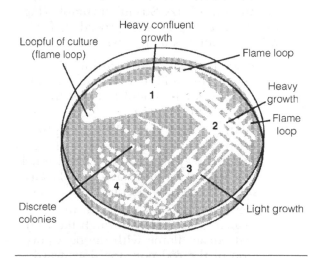

FIGURE 1 Four-way streak-plate inoculation

64

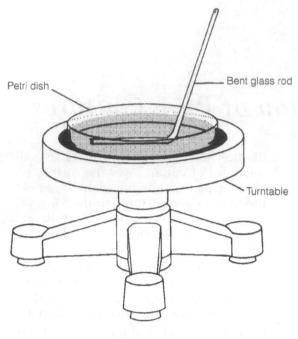

Petri dish — Bent glass rod

Turntable

FIGURE 2   Petri dish turntable

previously streaked areas. The flaming
of the loop at the points indicated is
    ffect the dilution of the culture so
        fewer organisms are streaked in
each area, resulting in the final
desired separation.

2. The **spread-plate** technique requires
    that a previously diluted mixture of mi-
    croorganisms be used. During inocula-
    tion, the cells are spread over the surface
    of a solid agar medium with a sterile,
    L-shaped bent rod while the Petri dish
    is spun on a "lazy-Susan" turntable (Fig-
    ure 2). The step-by-step procedure for
    this technique is as follows:

    a. Place the bent glass rod into the
        beaker and add a sufficient amount
        of 95% ethyl alcohol to cover the
        lower, bent portion.

    b. With a sterile loop, place a loopful of
        Micrococcus luteus culture in the cen-
        ter of the appropriately labeled nutri-
        ent agar plate that has been placed
        on the turntable. Replace the cover.

    c. Remove the glass rod from the
        beaker, and pass it through the Bun-
        sen burner flame with the bent por-
        tion of the rod pointing downward
        to prevent the burning alcohol from

running down your arm. Allow the
alcohol to burn off the rod completely. Cool the rod for 10 to
15 seconds.

    d. Remove the Petri dish cover and spin
        the turntable.

    e. While the turntable is spinning,
        lightly touch the sterile bent rod to
        the surface of the agar and move it
        back and forth. This will spread the
        culture over the agar surface.

    f. When the turntable comes to a stop,
        replace the cover. Immerse the rod in
        alcohol and reflame.

    g. In the absence of a turntable, turn
        the Petri dish manually and spread
        the culture with the sterile bent glass
        rod.

3. The **pour-plate** technique requires a
    serial dilution of the mixed culture by
    means of a loop or pipette. The diluted
    inoculum is then added to a molten agar
    medium in a Petri dish, mixed, and
    allowed to solidify.

MATERIALS

Cultures

24- to 48-hour nutrient broth cultures of a
mixture of one part *Serratia marcescens* and
three parts *Micrococcus luteus* and a mixture
of one part *Escherichia coli* and ten parts
Micrococcus luteus. For the spread-plate procedure, adjust the cultures to an optical density (O.D.) of 0.1 at 600 mμ.

Sources of mixed cultures from the environment could include cultures from a table
top, bathroom sink, water fountain, or inside
of an incubator. Each student should obtain
a mixed culture from one of the environmental sources listed above.

Media

Three trypticase soy agar plates per designated student group for each inoculation
technique to be performed.

Equipment

Bunsen burner, inoculating loop, turntable,
95% ethyl alcohol, 500-ml beaker, L-shaped
bent glass rod, glassware marking pencil,
culture tubes containing 1 ml of sterile

Techniques for Isolation of Pure Cultures

water, test tube rack, and sterile cotton swabs.

PROCEDURE

1. Following the procedures previously described, prepare a spread-plate and/or streak-plate inoculation of each test culture on an appropriately labeled plate.
2. Preparation of environmental mixed culture.
    a. Dampen a sterile cotton swab with sterile water. Wring out the excess water by pressing the wet swab against the walls of the tube.
    b. With the moistened cotton swab, obtain your mixed-culture specimen from one of the selected environmental sources.
    c. Place the contaminated swab back into the tube of sterile water. Mix gently and let stand for 5 minutes.
    d. Perform spread-plate and/or streak-plate inoculation on an appropriately labeled plate.
3. Incubate all plates in an inverted position for 48 to 72 hours at 25°C.

PART B: Isolation of Pure Cultures from a Spread-Plate or Streak-Plate Preparation

PURPOSE

To prepare a stock culture of an organism using isolates from the mixed cultures prepared on the agar streak-plate and/or the spread plate in Part A of this experiment.

PRINCIPLE

Once discrete, well-separated colonies develop on the surface of a nutrient agar plate culture, each may be picked up with a sterile needle and transferred to separate nutrient agar slants. Each of these new slant cultures represents the growth of a single bacterial species and is designated as a **pure or stock culture**.

MATERIALS

Cultures

Mixed-culture, nutrient agar streak-plate, and/or spread-plate preparations of S. marcescens and M. luteus, M. luteus and E. coli, and the environmental specimen plate from Part A.

Media

Four trypticase soy agar slants per designated student group.

Equipment

Bunsen burner, inoculating needle, and glassware marking pencil.

PROCEDURE

1. Aseptically transfer, from visibly discrete colonies, the yellow M. luteus, the white E. coli, the red S. marcescens, and a discrete colony from the environmental agar plate specimen to the appropriately labeled agar slants as shown in Figure 3.
2. Incubate the cultures for 48 to 72 hours at 25°C.

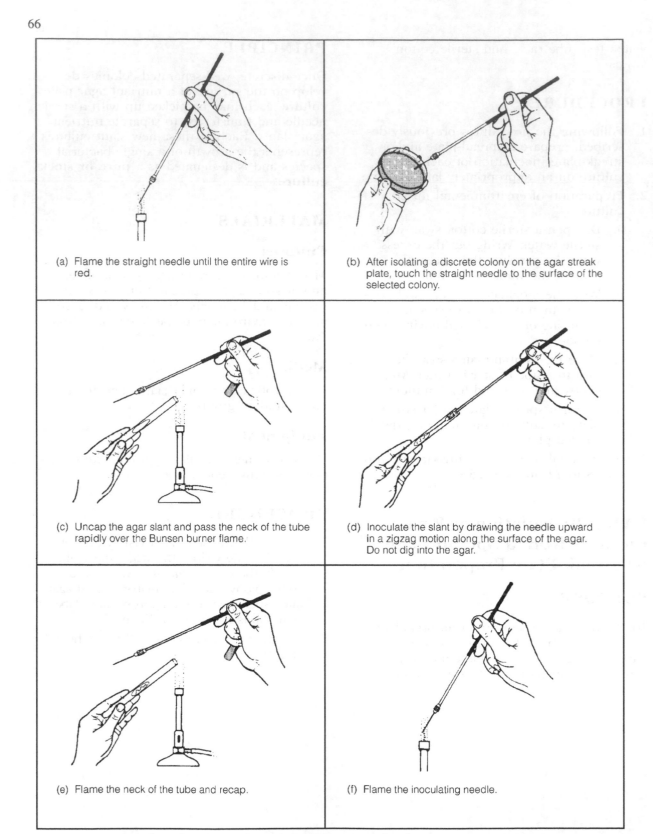

(a) Flame the straight needle until the entire wire is red.

(b) After isolating a discrete colony on the agar streak plate, touch the straight needle to the surface of the selected colony.

(c) Uncap the agar slant and pass the neck of the tube rapidly over the Bunsen burner flame.

(d) Inoculate the slant by drawing the needle upward in a zigzag motion along the surface of the agar. Do not dig into the agar.

(e) Flame the neck of the tube and recap.

(f) Flame the inoculating needle.

FIGURE 3 Procedure for the preparation of a pure culture

Techniques for Isolation of Pure Cultures

OBSERVATIONS AND RESULTS

PART A: Isolation of Discrete Colonies from a Mixed Culture

Examine all agar plate cultures to identify the distribution of the colonies. Record your results in the charts below.

1. Make a drawing of the distribution of colonies appearing on each of the agar plate cultures.
2. Select two discrete colonies that differ in appearance on each of the agar plate cultures. Using Figure 1, describe each colony as to its:
   a. Form: Circular, irregular, or spreading.
   b. Elevation: Flat, slightly raised, or markedly raised.
   c. Pigmentation.
   d. Size: Pinpoint, small, medium, or large.
3. Retain the mixed-culture plates to perform Part B of this experiment.

✚ *Refer to the color-plate insert for illustration of streak-plate technique.*

Spread-Plate Technique				
	S. marcescens and *M. luteus*		*M. luteus* and *E. coli*	
Draw the colonies that appear on agar plate.				
Colony description:	Isolate 1	Isolate 2	Isolate 1	Isolate 2
Form	_____	_____	_____	_____
Elevation	_____	_____	_____	_____
Pigmentation	_____	_____	_____	_____
Size	_____	_____	_____	_____

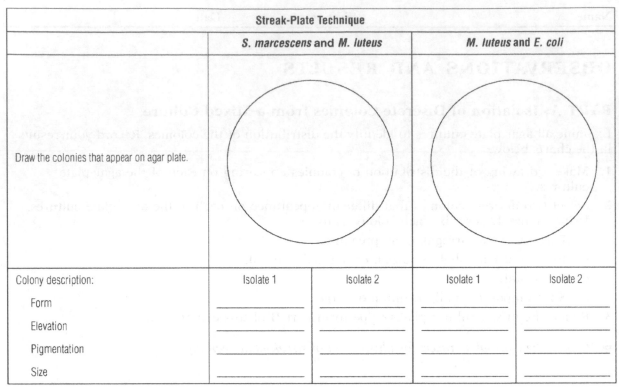

Streak-Plate Technique				
	S. marcescens and *M. luteus*		*M. luteus* and *E. coli*	
Draw the colonies that appear on agar plate.				
Colony description:	Isolate 1	Isolate 2	Isolate 1	Isolate 2
Form	_____	_____	_____	_____
Elevation	_____	_____	_____	_____
Pigmentation	_____	_____	_____	_____
Size	_____	_____	_____	_____

Environmental Specimen		
	Spread-Plate Technique	Streak-Plate Technique
Draw the colonies that appear on agar plate.		
Colony description:		
Form	_____	_____
Elevation	_____	_____
Pigmentation	_____	_____
Size	_____	_____

Techniques for Isolation of Pure Cultures

PART B: Isolation of Pure Cultures from a
Spread-Plate or Streak-Plate Preparation

1. Draw and indicate the type of growth of each pure-culture isolate.
2. Observe the color of the growth and record its pigmentation.
3. Indicate the names of the isolated organisms.

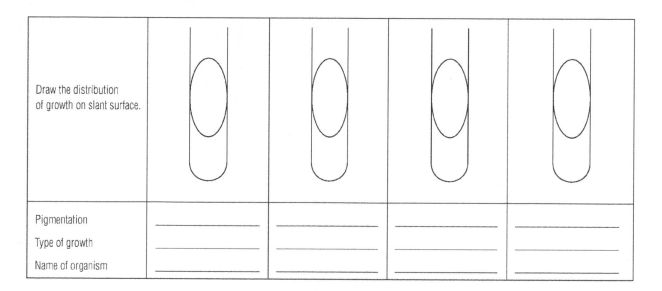

Draw the distribution of growth on slant surface.				
Pigmentation	_____	_____	_____	_____
Type of growth	_____	_____	_____	_____
Name of organism	_____	_____	_____	_____

¯EVIEW QUESTIONS

1. Can a pure culture be prepared directly from a mixed-broth or a mixed–agar-slant culture? Explain.

2. Observation of a streak-plate culture shows more growth in Quadrant 4 than in Quadrant 3. Account for this observation.

Techniques for Isolation of Pure Cultures

8

Microscopic Examination of Living Bacterial Preparations

PURPOSE

To perform the hanging-drop procedure for microscopic observation of living bacteria.

PRINCIPLE

Bacteria, because of their small size and a refractive index that closely approximates that of water, do not lend themselves readily to microscopic examination in a living, unstained state. Examination of living microorganisms is useful, however, to

1. Observe cell activities such as motility and binary fission.
2. Observe the natural sizes and shapes of the cells, since **heat fixation** (the rapid passage of the smear over the Bunsen burner flame) and exposure to chemicals during staining cause some degree of distortion.

In this experiment, you will use a mixed culture of *Pseudomonas aeruginosa*, *Bacillus cereus*, and *Staphylococcus aureus*, or individual cultures of the above-listed organisms, for the hanging-drop preparation (Figure 1).

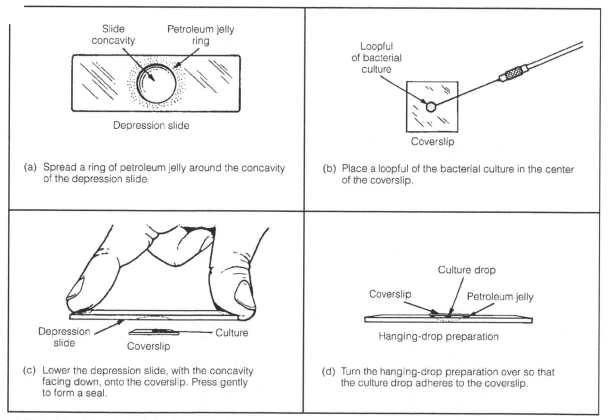

(a) Spread a ring of petroleum jelly around the concavity of the depression slide.

(b) Place a loopful of the bacterial culture in the center of the coverslip.

(c) Lower the depression slide, with the concavity facing down, onto the coverslip. Press gently to form a seal.

(d) Turn the hanging-drop preparation over so that the culture drop adheres to the coverslip.

FIGURE 1   Hanging-drop preparation

You will observe the preparation(s) microscopically for differences in the sizes and shapes of the cells, as well as for motility, a self-directed movement. It is essential to differentiate between actual motility and **Brownian movement**, a vibratory movement of the cells due to their bombardment by water molecules in the suspension.

MATERIALS

Cultures

24-hour mixed broth culture of *P. aeruginosa*, *B. cereus*, and *S. aureus*; or 24-hour individual broth cultures of the above-listed organisms.

Equipment

Bunsen burner, inoculating loop, depression slide, coverslip, microscope, petroleum jelly, and cotton swabs.

PROCEDURE

Perform the following steps for each culture provided in this experiment.

1. With a cotton swab, apply a ring of petroleum jelly around the concavity of the depression slide.
2. Using sterile technique, place a loopful of the mixed culture in the center of a clean coverslip.
3. Place the depression slide, with the concave surface facing down, over the coverslip so that the depression covers the drop of culture. Press the slide gently to form a seal between the slide and the coverslip.
4. Quickly turn the slide right side up so that the drop continues to adhere to the inner surface of the coverslip.
5. For microscopic examination, first focus in on the drop of culture under the low-power objective with reduced light. Place a drop of oil on the coverslip and use the oil-immersion objective for detailed observation.

Name   Section   Date

OBSERVATIONS AND RESULTS

1. Examine the hanging-drop preparation to determine shape and motility of the different bacteria present. Record your results in the chart below.

Organisms	Shape	True Motility or Brownian Movement
S. aureus		
P. aeruginosa		
B. cereus		

2. Draw a representative field:

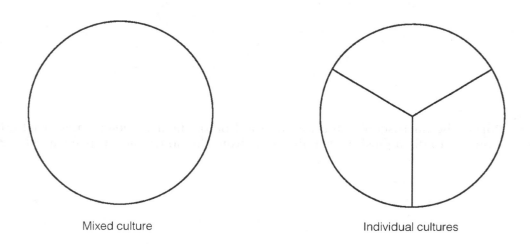

Mixed culture   Individual cultures

REVIEW QUESTIONS

1. Why are living, unstained bacterial preparations more difficult to observe microscopically than stained preparations?

Microscopic Examination of Living Bacterial Preparations

2. For what purposes is it essential that living specimens be observed?

3. Distinguish between true motility and Brownian movement.

4. During the microscopic observation of a drop of stagnant pond water, what criteria would you use to distinguish viable life forms from the nonviable, suspended debris?

Bacterial Staining

PURPOSES

To become familiar with
1. The chemical and theoretical bases of biological staining.
2. Manipulative techniques of smear preparation.
3. Procedures for simple staining and negative staining.
4. Performing differential staining procedures such as the Gram, acid-fast, capsule, and spore stains.

INTRODUCTION

Visualization of microorganisms in the living state is quite difficult, not only because they are minute, but also because they are transparent and practically colorless when suspended in an aqueous medium. To study their properties and to divide microorganisms into specific groups for diagnostic purposes, biological stains and staining procedures in conjunction with light microscopy have become major tools in microbiology.

Chemically, a stain (dye) may be defined as an organic compound containing a benzene ring plus a chromophore and auxochrome group (Figure 1).

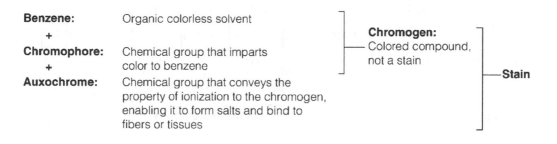

Benzene: Organic colorless solvent

\+

Chromophore: Chemical group that imparts color to benzene

\+

Auxochrome: Chemical group that conveys the property of ionization to the chromogen, enabling it to form salts and bind to fibers or tissues

Chromogen: Colored compound, not a stain

Stain

FIGURE 1   Chemical composition of a strain

The stain picric acid may be used to illustrate this definition:

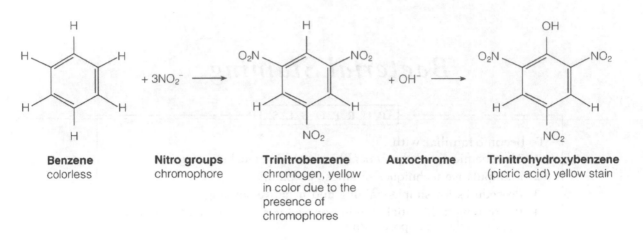

The ability of a stain to bind to macromolecular cellular components such as proteins or nucleic acids depends on the electrical charge found on the chromogen portion, as well as on the cellular component to be stained.

Acidic stains are anionic, which means that, on ionization of the stain, the chromogen portion exhibits a negative charge and therefore has a strong affinity for the positive constituents of the cell. Proteins, positively charged cellular components, will readily bind to and accept the color of the negatively charged, anionic chromogen of an acidic stain. Structurally, picric acid is an example of an acidic stain that produces an anionic chromogen as illustrated:

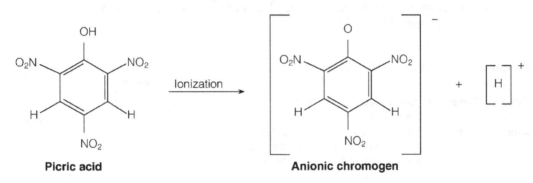

Basic stains are cationic, because on ionization the chromogen portion exhibits a positive charge and therefore has a strong affinity for the negative constituents of the cell. Nucleic acids, negatively charged cellular components, will readily bind to and accept the color of the positively charged, cationic chromogen of a basic stain. Structurally, methylene blue is a basic stain that produces a cationic chromogen as illustrated:

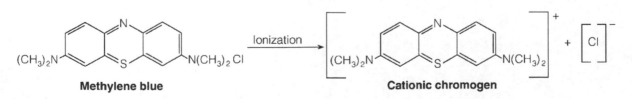

Bacterial Staining

Figure 2 is a summary of acidic and basic stains.

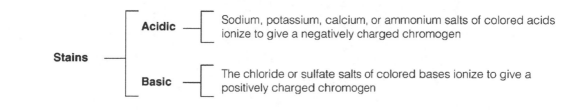

FIGURE 2 Acidic and basic stains

Basic stains are more commonly used for bacterial staining. The presence of a negative charge on the bacterial surface acts to repel most acidic stains and thus prevent their penetration into the cell.

Numerous staining techniques are available for visualization, differentiation, and separation of bacteria in terms of morphological characteristics and cellular structures. A summary of commonly used procedures and their purposes is outlined in Figure 3.

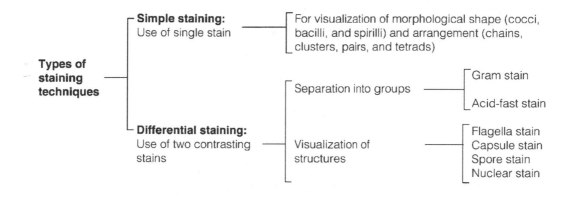

FIGURE 3 Staining techniques

Bacterial Staining

Preparation of Smears and Simple Staining

Objectives

After completing this exercise, you should be able to:

1. Make and fix a smear.
2. List the advantages of staining microorganisms.
3. Explain the basic mechanism of staining.
4. Perform a simple direct stain.

Background

Most stains used in microbiology are synthetic aniline (coal tar derivative) dyes derived from benzene. The dyes are usually salts, although a few are acids or bases, composed of charged colored ions. The ion that is colored is referred to as a **chromophore.** For example,

Methylene blue chloride ⇋ Methylene blue⁺ + Cl⁻
(Chromophore)

If the chromophore is a positive ion like the methylene blue in the equation shown, the stain is considered a **basic stain;** if a negative ion, it is an **acidic stain.** Most bacteria are stained when a basic stain permeates the cell wall and adheres by weak ionic bonds to the negative charges of the bacterial cell.

Staining procedures that use only one stain are called **simple stains.** A simple stain that stains the bacteria is a **direct stain,** and a simple stain that stains the background but leaves the bacteria unstained is a **negative stain.** Simple stains can be used to determine cell morphology, size, and arrangement.

Before bacteria can be stained, a smear must be made and fixed. A **smear** is made by spreading a bacterial suspension on a clean slide and allowing it to air dry. The dry smear is passed through a Bunsen burner flame several times to **heat fix** the bacteria. Heat fixing in a flame may not kill all the bacteria. Alternatively, the dry smear can be placed on a 60°C slide warmer for 10 minutes or chemically fixed. To **chemically fix** the bacteria, cover the smear with 95% methyl alcohol for 1 minute. Fixing denatures bacterial enzymes, preventing them from digesting cell parts, which causes the cell to break, a process called *autolysis.* Fixing also enhances the adherence of bacterial cells to the microscope slide.

Materials

Methylene blue

Wash bottle of distilled water

Slide

Inoculating loop

Cultures

Staphylococcus epidermidis slant

Bacillus megaterium broth

Techniques Required

Compound light microscopy

Inoculating loop

Procedure

1. Clean your slide well with abrasive soap or cleanser; rinse and dry. Handle clean slides by the end or edge. Use a marker to make two dime-sized circles on each slide, on the bottom of the slide so they will not wash off. Label each circle according to the bacterial culture used.
2. For the bacterial culture on solid media, place 1 or 2 loopfuls of distilled water in the center of one circle, using the inoculating loop. Which bacterium is on a solid medium? _____
3. Sterilize your inoculating loop by holding it in the hottest part of the flame (at the edge of the inner blue area) until it is red-hot (see the figure on the facing page). The entire wire should get red. Allow the loop to cool so that bacteria picked up with the loop won't be killed. Allow the loop to cool without touching it. Cooling takes about 30 seconds. You will determine the appropriate time with a little practice.

> ☣ **The loop must be cool before inserting it into a medium. A loop that is too hot will spatter the medium and move bacteria into the air.**

4. Smear preparation (Figure 1).
   a. Using the cooled loop, scrape a *small* amount of the culture off the slant. If you hear the sizzle of boiling water when you touch the agar

(a) Mark the smear areas with a marking pencil on the underside of a clean slide.

FROM SOLID MEDIUM   FROM LIQUID MEDIUM

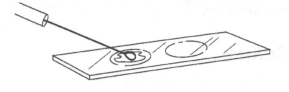

(b) Place 1 or 2 loopfuls of water on the slide.

(d) Place 2 or 3 loopfuls of the liquid culture on the slide with a sterile loop.

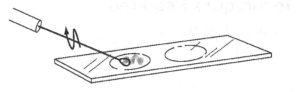

(c) Transfer a very small amount of the culture with a sterile loop. Mix with the water on the slide.

(e) Spread the bacteria within the ring.

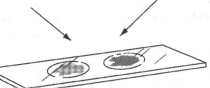

(f) Allow the smears to air dry at room temperature.

or

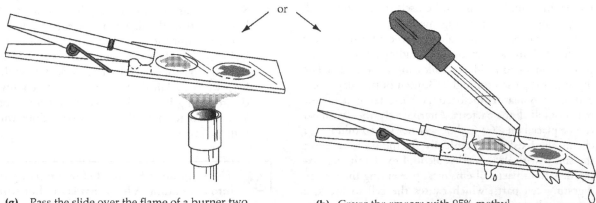

(g) Pass the slide over the flame of a burner two or three times.

(h) Cover the smears with 95% methyl alcohol for one minute, then let the smears air dry.

Figure 1

Preparing a bacterial smear.

with the loop, reflame your loop and begin again. Why? _____
Try not to gouge the agar. Emulsify (to a milky suspension) the cells in the drop of water, and spread the suspension to fill a majority of the circle. The smear should look like diluted skim milk. Flame your loop again.

b. Make a smear of bacteria from the broth culture on the other circle. *Do not use water,* because the bacteria are already suspended in water. Flick the tube of broth culture lightly with your finger to resuspend sedimented bacteria, and place 2 or 3 loopfuls of the culture in the circle. Flame your loop between each loopful. Spread the culture within the circle (Figure 2).

c. Flame your loop.

> ☣ **Always flame your loop after using it and before setting it down.**

d. Let the smears dry. *Do not* blow on the slide, as this will move the bacterial suspension. *Do not* flame the slide, as flaming will distort the cells' shapes.

e. Hold the slide with a clothespin and fix the smears by one of the following methods (Figure 1g or h):
   (1) Pass the slide quickly through the blue flame two or three times.
   (2) Cover the smear with 95% methyl alcohol for 1 minute. Tip the slide to let the alcohol run off, and let the slide air dry before staining. Do not fix until the smears are completely dry. Why? _____
   _____

5. Staining (Figure 3).
   a. Use a clothespin to hold the slide, or place it on a staining rack.
   b. Cover the smear with methylene blue and leave it for 30 to 60 seconds (Figure 3a).
   c. Carefully wash the excess stain off with distilled water from a wash bottle. Let the water run down the tilted slide (Figure 3b).

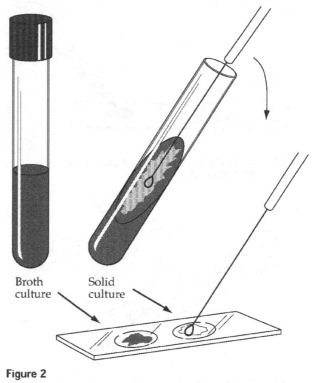

Figure 2
A loopful of microbial suspension is transferred to a slide.

Broth culture   Solid culture

   d. Gently blot the smear with a paper towel or absorbent paper and let it dry (Figure 3c and d).

6. Examine your stained smears microscopically using the low, high-dry, and oil immersion objectives. Put the oil *directly* on the smear; coverslips are not needed. Record your observations with labeled drawings.

7. Blot the oil from the objective lens with lens paper, and return your microscope to its proper location. Clean your slides well, or save them as described in step 8.

8. Stained bacterial slides can be stored in a slide box. Remove the oil from the slide by blotting it with a paper towel. Any residual oil won't matter.

(a) Cover the smear with methylene blue for 30 seconds.

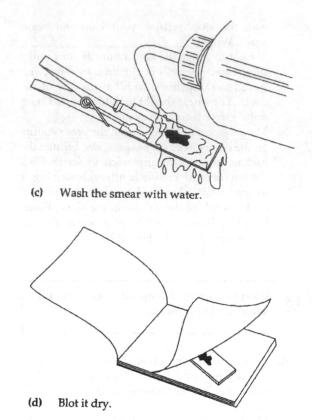

(c) Wash the smear with water.

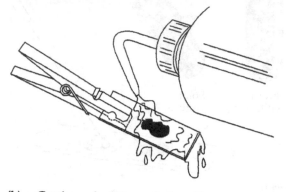

(b) Gently wash off the methylene blue with water by squirting the water so it runs through the smear.

(d) Blot it dry.

Figure 3

Simple staining.

Preparation of Smears and Simple Staining

LABORATORY REPORT

Name_____

Date_____

Lab Section _____

Purpose _____

_____

_____

Data

Staphylococcus epidermidis

Sketch a few bacteria under
1000× magnification.

Morphology (shape): _____

Arrangement of cells
relative to one another: _____

Bacillus megaterium

Sketch a few bacteria under
1000× magnification.

Morphology (shape): _____

Arrangement of cells
relative to one another: _____

Questions

1. Which bacterium is a rod? _____

2. Of what value is a simple stain? _____

   _____

3. What is the purpose of fixing the smear? _____

   _____

4. In heat fixing, what would happen if too much heat were applied? _____

   _____

Critical Thinking

1. Methylene blue can be prepared as a basic stain or an acidic stain. How would the pH affect the staining of bacteria?

2. C   s other than methylene blue be used for direct staining? Briefly explain.

3. Bacteria can be seen without staining. Why then was Koch's recommendation for fixing and staining important for microbiology?

10

Gram Stain

PURPOSES

To become familiar with

1. The chemical and theoretical bases for differential staining procedures.
2. The chemical basis of the Gram stain.
3. Performance of the procedure for differentiating between the two principal groups of bacteria: gram-positive and gram-negative.

PRINCIPLE

Differential staining requires the use of at least three chemical reagents that are applied sequentially to a heat-fixed smear. The first reagent is called the **primary stain**. Its function is to impart its color to all cells. In order to establish a color contrast, the second reagent used is the **decolorizing agent**. Based on the chemical composition of cellular components, the decolorizing agent may or may not remove the primary stain from the entire cell or only from certain cell structures. The final reagent, the **counterstain**, has a contrasting color to that of the primary stain. Following decolorization, if the primary stain is not washed out, the counterstain cannot be absorbed and the cell or its

components will retain the color of the primary stain. If the primary stain is removed, the decolorized cellular components will accept and assume the contrasting color of the counterstain. In this way, cell types or their structures can be distinguished from each other on the basis of the stain that is retained.

The most important differential stain used in bacteriology is the **Gram stain**, named after Dr. Christian Gram. It divides bacterial cells into two major groups, gram-positive and gram-negative, which makes it an essential tool for classification and differentiation of microorganisms. The Gram stain reaction is based on the difference in the chemical composition of bacterial cell walls. Gram-positive cells have a thick peptidoglycan layer, whereas the peptidoglycan layer in gram-negative cells is much thinner and surrounded by outer lipid-containing layers. Early experiments have shown that if the gram-positive cell is denuded of its cell wall by the action of lysozyme or penicillin, the gram-positive cell will stain gram-negative. The Gram stain uses four different reagents. Descriptions of these reagents and their mechanisms of action follow. Figure 1 shows the microscopic observation of the cell at each step of the Gram staining procedure.

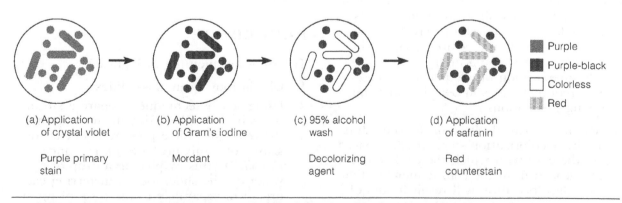

				■ Purple
				■ Purple-black
				□ Colorless
				▨ Red

(a) Application of crystal violet

Purple primary stain

(b) Application of Gram's iodine

Mordant

(c) 95% alcohol wash

Decolorizing agent

(d) Application of safranin

Red counterstain

FIGURE 1   **Microscopic observation of cells following the Gram staining procedure**

Primary Stain

Crystal Violet (Hucker's) This violet stain is used first and stains all cells purple.

Mordant

Gram's Iodine This reagent serves as a mordant, a substance that increases the cells' affinity for a stain. It does this by binding to the primary stain, thus forming an insoluble complex. The resultant crystal-violet-iodine (CV-I) complex serves to intensify the color of the stain. At this point, all cells will appear purple-black.

Decolorizing Agent

Ethyl Alcohol, 95% This reagent serves a dual function as a protein-dehydrating agent and as a lipid solvent. Its action is determined by two factors, the concentration of lipids and the thickness of the peptidoglycan layer in bacterial cell walls. In gram-negative cells, the alcohol increases the porosity of the cell wall by dissolving the lipids in the outer layers. Thus, the CV-I complex can be more easily removed from the thinner and less highly cross-linked peptidoglycan layer. There   he washing-out effect of the alcoho. ....litates the release of the unbound CV-I complex, leaving the cells colorless or unstained. The much thicker peptidoglycan layer in gram-positive cells is responsible for the more stringent retention of the CV-I complex, as the pores are made smaller due to the dehydrating effect of the alcohol. Thus the tightly bound primary stain complex is difficult to remove, and the cells remain purple.

Counterstain

Safranin This is the final reagent, used to stain red those cells that have been previously decolorized. Since only gram-negative cells undergo decolorization, they may now absorb the counterstain. Gram-positive cells retain the purple color of the primary stain.

The preparation of adequately stained smears requires that you bear in mind the following precautions:

1. The most critical phase of the procedure is the decolorization step, which is based on the ease with which the CV-I complex is released from the cell. Remember that over-decolorization will result in loss of the primary stain, causing gram-positive organisms to appear gram-negative. Under-decolorization, however, will not completely remove the CV-I complex, causing gram-negative organisms to appear gram-positive. Strict adherence to all instructions will help remedy part of the difficulty, but individual experience and practice are the keys to correct decolorization.

2. It is imperative that, between applications of the reagents, slides be thoroughly washed under running water or water applied with an eyedropper. This removes excess reagent and prepares the slide for application of the subsequent reagent.

3. The best Gram stained preparations are made with fresh cultures, that is, not older than 24 hours. As cultures age, especially in the case of gram-positive cells, the organisms tend to lose their ability to retain the primary stain and may appear to be **gram-variable**; that is, some cells will appear purple, while others will appear red.

MATERIALS

Cultures

24-hour nutrient agar slant cultures of *Escherichia coli*, *Staphylococcus aureus*, and *Bacillus cereus*.

Reagents

Crystal violet, Gram's iodine, 95% ethyl alcohol, and safranin.

Equipment

Bunsen burner, inoculating loop or needle, staining tray, glass slides, bibulous paper, lens paper, and microscope.

PROCEDURE

The steps are pictured in Figure 2.

1. Obtain four clean glass slides.
2. Using sterile technique, prepare a smear of each of the three organisms and on the remaining slide prepare a smear consisting of a mixture of *S. aureus* and *E. coli*. Do this by placing a drop of water on the slide, then transferring each organism separately to the drop of water with a sterile, cooled loop. Mix and

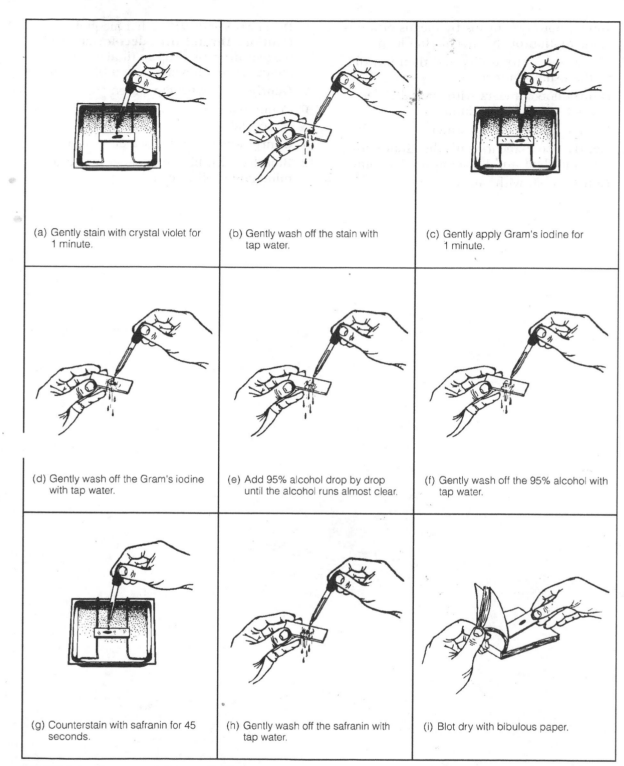

(a) Gently stain with crystal violet for 1 minute.

(b) Gently wash off the stain with tap water.

(c) Gently apply Gram's iodine for 1 minute.

(d) Gently wash off the Gram's iodine with tap water.

(e) Add 95% alcohol drop by drop until the alcohol runs almost clear.

(f) Gently wash off the 95% alcohol with tap water.

(g) Counterstain with safranin for 45 seconds.

(h) Gently wash off the safranin with tap water.

(i) Blot dry with bibulous paper.

FIGURE 2 Gram staining procedure

Gram Stain

spread both organisms by means of a circular motion of the inoculating loop.

3. Allow smears to air-dry and then heat fix in the usual manner.

4. **Gently** flood smears with crystal violet and let stand for 1 minute.

5. **Gently** wash with tap water.

6. **Gently** flood smears with the Gram's iodine mordant and let stand for 1 minute.

7. **Gently** wash with tap water.

8. Decolorize with 95% ethyl alcohol. **Caution: Do not over-decolorize.** Add reagent drop by drop until alcohol runs almost clear, showing only a blue tinge.

9. **Gently** wash with tap water.

10. Counterstain with safranin for 45 seconds.

11. **Gently** wash with tap water.

12. Blot dry with bibulous paper and examine under oil immersion.

Name   Section   Date

OBSERVATIONS AND RESULTS

Following your observation of all slides under oil immersion, record your results in the chart.

1. Make a drawing of a representative microscopic field.
2. Describe the cells according to their morphology and arrangement.
3. Describe the color of the stained cells.
4. Classify the organism as to the Gram reaction: gram-positive or gram-negative.

✚ *Refer to the color-plate insert for illustration of this staining procedure.*

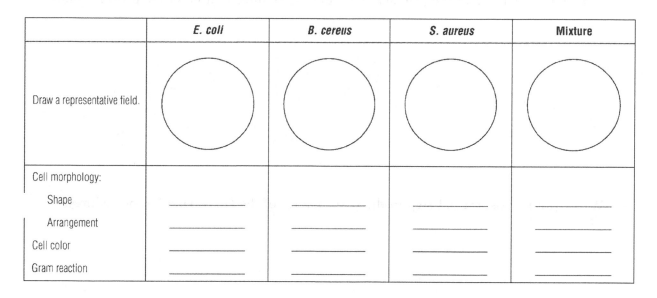

	E. coli	*B. cereus*	*S. aureus*	Mixture
Draw a representative field.				
Cell morphology: Shape				
Arrangement				
Cell color				
Gram reaction				

REVIEW QUESTIONS

1. What are the advantages of differential staining procedures over the simple staining technique?

2. Cite the purpose of each of the following reagents in a differential staining procedure.
    a. Primary stain:

    b. Counterstain:

Gram Stain

c. Decolorizing agent:

d. Mordant:

3. Why is it essential that the primary stain and the counterstain be of contrasting colors?

4. W   s the most crucial step in the performance of the Gram staining procedures?
   E>   .

5. ✎ Because of a snowstorm, your regular laboratory session was cancelled and the Gram staining procedure was performed on cultures incubated for a longer period of time. Examination of the stained *Bacillus cereus* slides revealed a great deal of color variability, ranging from an intense blue to shades of pink. Account for this result.

Gram Stain

Acid-Fast Staining

Objectives

After completing this exercise, you should be able to:

1. Apply the acid-fast procedure.
2. Explain what is occurring during the acid-fast staining procedure.
3. Perform and interpret an acid-fast stain.

Background

The **acid-fast stain** is a differential stain. In 1882 Paul Ehrlich discovered that *Mycobacterium tuberculosis* (the causative agent of tuberculosis) retained the primary stain even after washing with an acid-alcohol mixture. (We hope you can appreciate the phenomenal strides that were made in microbiology in the 1880s. Most of the staining and culturing techniques used today originated during that time.) Most bacteria are decolorized by acid-alcohol, with only the families Mycobacteriaceae, Nocardiaceae, Goroniaceae, and Tsukamurellaceae (*Bergey's Manual**) being acid-fast. The acid-fast technique has great value as a diagnostic procedure because both *Mycobacterium* and *Nocardia* contain **pathogenic** (disease-causing) species.

The cell walls of acid-fast organisms contain a wax-like lipid called **mycolic acid,** which renders the cell wall impermeable to most stains. The cell wall is so impermeable, in fact, that a clinical specimen is usually treated with strong sodium hydroxide to remove debris and contaminating bacteria prior to culturing mycobacteria. The mycobacteria are not killed by this procedure.

Today, the techniques developed by Franz Ziehl and Friedrich Neelsen and by Joseph J. Kinyoun are the most widely used acid-fast stains. In the **Ziehl–Neelsen procedure,** the smear is flooded with carbolfuchsin (a dark red dye containing 5% phenol), which has a high affinity for a chemical component of the bacterial cell. The smear is heated to facilitate penetration of the stain into the bacteria. The stained smears are washed with an acid-alcohol mixture that easily decolorizes most bacteria except the acid-fast microbes. Methylene blue is then used as a counterstain to enable you to observe the non-acid-fast organisms. In the **Kinyoun modification**, called a *cold stain*, the concentrations of phenol and carbolfuchsin are increased so heating isn't necessary.

The mechanism of the acid-fast stain is probably the result of the relative solubility of carbolfuchsin and the impermeability of the cell wall. Fuchsin is more soluble in carbolic acid (phenol) than in water, and carbolic acid solubilizes more easily in lipids than in acid-alcohol. Therefore, carbolfuchsin has a higher affinity for lipids than for acid-alcohol and will remain with the cell wall when washed with acid-alcohol.

Materials

Acid-fast staining reagents:
    Kinyoun's carbolfuchsin
    Acid-alcohol
    Methylene blue

Wash bottle of distilled water

Slide

Cultures

Mycobacterium phlei

Escherichia coli

Demonstration Slides

Acid-fast sputum slides

Techniques Required

Compound light microscopy

Smear preparation

Simple staining

Procedure

1. Prepare and fix a smear of each culture.
2. Cover the smears with carbolfuchsin and leave them for 5 minutes (Figure 1a).
3. Gently wash the slide with distilled water from a wash bottle. Do not squirt water directly onto the smear (Figure 1b).

*Bergey's Manual of Systematic Bacteriology, 2nd ed., 5 vols. (2000) is the standard reference for classification of prokaryotic organisms. *Bergey's Manual of Determinative Bacteriology,* 9th ed. (1994) is the standard reference for identification of culturable bacteria and archaea.

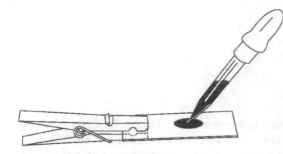

(a)   Cover the smear with carbolfuchsin
      for 5 minutes.

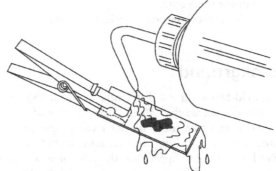

(e)   Cover the smear with methylene
      blue for 1 minute.

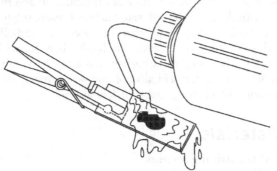

(b)   Gently wash off the carbolfuchsin with water
      by squirting the water so it runs through
      the smear.

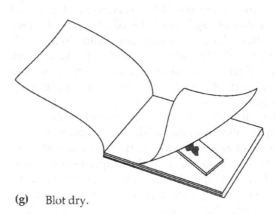

(f)   Wash with water.

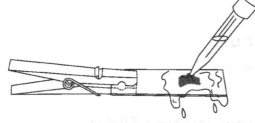

(c)   Wash the smear with acid-alcohol for
      1 minute.

(g)   Blot dry.

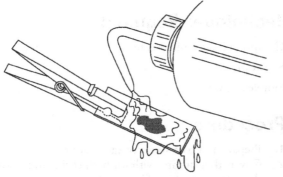

(d)   Gently wash the smear with water.

Figure 1
Preparing an acid-fast stain.

4. Without drying it, wash the smear with decolorizer for 1 minute or until no more red color runs off when the slide is tipped (Figure 1c).

5. Wash the smear carefully with distilled water (Figure 1d).

6. Counterstain the smear for about 1 minute with methylene blue (Figure 1e).

7. Wash the smear with distilled water and blot it dry (Figure 1f and g).

8. Examine the acid-fast stained slide microscopically and record your observations.

9. Observe the demonstration slides.

Acid-Fast Staining

LABORATORY REPORT

Name _____

Date _____

Lab Section _____

Purpose _____

_____

_____

Data

Sketch a few
bacteria (1000×).

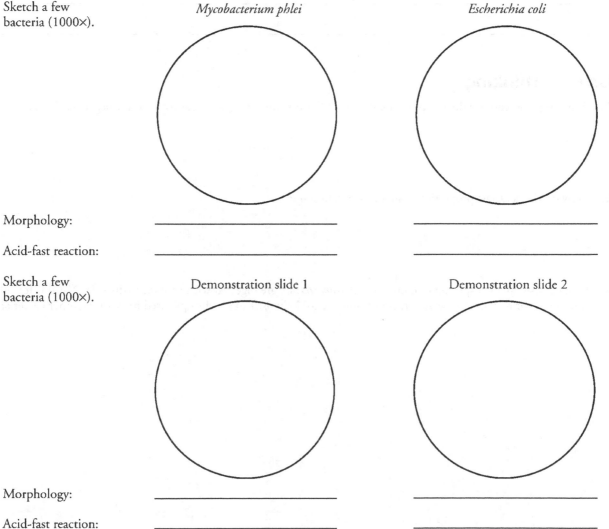

Mycobacterium phlei

Escherichia coli

Morphology: _____   _____

Acid-fast reaction: _____   _____

Sketch a few
bacteria (1000×).

Demonstration slide 1

Demonstration slide 2

Morphology: _____   _____

Acid-fast reaction: _____   _____

Questions

1. What are the large stained areas on the sputum slide? _____

_____

_____

2. What is the decolorizing agent in the Gram stain? _____

   In the acid-fast stain? _____

3. What diseases are diagnosed using the acid-fast procedure? _____

_____

_____

4. What is phenol (carbolic acid), and what is its *usual* application? _____

_____

_____

Crit   Thinking

1. Assuming you could stain any cell, would an acid-fast organism be gram-positive or gram-negative? Explain.

2. How do the acid-fast properties relate to the Gram stain?

3. Clinical specimens suspected of containing *Mycobacterium* are digested with sodium hydroxide (NaOH) for 30 minutes prior to staining. Why is this technique used? Why isn't this technique used for staining other bacteria?

12

Differential Staining for Visualization of Bacterial Cell Structures

PURPOSES

To become familiar with

1. The chemical basis for the spore and capsule stains.
2. Performance of the procedure for differentiation between bacterial spore and vegetative cell forms.
3. Performance of the procedure to distinguish capsular material from the bacterial cell.

PART A: Spore Stain (Schaeffer-Fulton Method)

PRINCIPLE

Members of the anaerobic genera *Clostridium* and *Desulfotomaculum* and the aerobic genus *Bacillus* are examples of organisms that have the capacity to exist either as metabolically active **vegetative cells** or as highly resistant, metabolically inactive cell types called **spores**. When environmental conditions become unfavorable for continuing vegetative cellular activities, particularly with the exhaustion of a nutritional carbon source, these cells have the capacity to undergo **sporogenesis** and give rise to a new intracellular structure called the **endospore**, which is surrounded by impervious layers called spore coats. As conditions continue to worsen, the endospore is released from the degenerating vegetative cell and becomes an independent cell called a **spore**. Because of the chemical composition of spore layers, the spore is resistant to the deleterious effects of excessive heat, freezing, radiation, desiccation, and chemical agents, as well as to the commonly employed microbiological stains. With the return of favorable environmental conditions, the free spore

may revert to a metabolically active and less resistant vegetative cell through **germination** (see Figure 1). It should be emphasized that sporogenesis and germination are not means of reproduction but merely mechanisms that ensure cell survival under all environmental conditions.

In practice, the spore stain uses two different reagents.

Primary Stain

Malachite Green Unlike most vegetative cell types that stain by common procedures, the spore, because of its impervious coat, will not accept the primary stain easily. For further penetration, the application of heat is required. After the primary stain is applied and the smear is heated, both the vegetative cell and spore will appear green.

Decolorizing Agent

Water Once the spore accepts the malachite green, it cannot be decolorized by tap water, which removes only the excess primary stain. The spore remains green. On the other hand, the stain does not demonstrate a strong affinity for vegetative cell components; the water removes it, and these cells will be colorless.

Counterstain

Safranin This contrasting red stain is used as the second reagent to color the decolorized vegetative cells, which will absorb the counterstain and appear red. The spores retain the green of the primary stain.

MATERIALS

Cultures

48- to 72-hour nutrient agar slant culture of *Bacillus cereus* and thioglycollate culture of *Clostridium butyricum*.

From *Microbiology: A Laboratory Manual*, Sixth Edition, James G. Cappuccino and Natalie Sherman. Copyright © 2002 Pearson Education, Inc., publishing as Benjamin Cummings. All rights reserved.

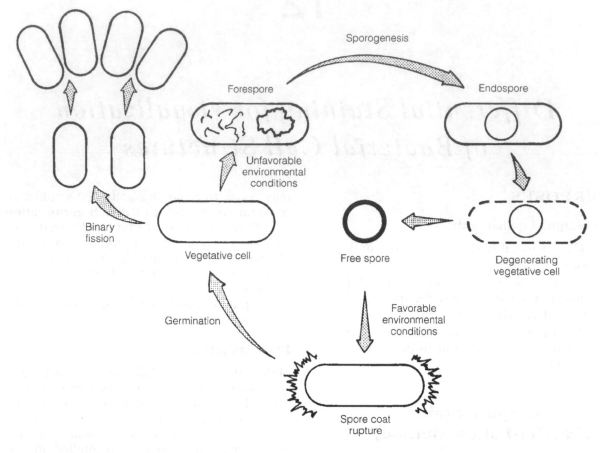

FIGURE 1 Life cycle of a spore-forming bacterium

Reagents

Malachite green and safranin.

Equipment

Bunsen burner, hot plate, staining tray, inoculating loop, glass slides, bibulous paper, lens paper, and microscope.

PROCEDURE

The steps are pictured in Figure 2.

1. Obtain two clean glass slides.
2. Make individual smears in the usual manner using sterile technique.
3. Allow smear to air-dry, and heat fix in the usual manner.
4. Flood smears with malachite green and place on a warm hot plate, allowing the preparation to steam for 2 to 3 minutes. **Caution: Do not allow stain to evaporate; replenish stain as needed.** Prevent the stain from boiling by adjusting the hot plate temperature.
5. Remove slides from hot plate, cool, and wash under running tap water.
6. Counterstain with safranin for 30 seconds.
7. Wash with tap water.
8. Blot dry with bibulous paper and examine under oil immersion.

PART B: Capsule Stain

PRINCIPLE

A **capsule** is a gelatinous outer layer that is secreted by the cell and that surrounds and adheres to the cell wall. It is not common to all organisms. Cells that have a heavy capsule are generally virulent and capable of producing disease, since the structure protects bacteria against the normal phagocytic

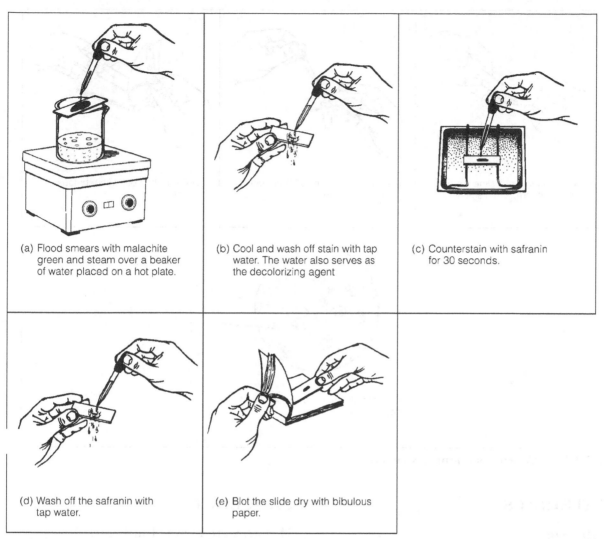

(a) Flood smears with malachite green and steam over a beaker of water placed on a hot plate.

(b) Cool and wash off stain with tap water. The water also serves as the decolorizing agent

(c) Counterstain with safranin for 30 seconds.

(d) Wash off the safranin with tap water.

(e) Blot the slide dry with bibulous paper.

FIGURE 2 Spore staining procedure

activities of host cells. Chemically, the capsular material is a polysaccharide, a glycoprotein, or a polypeptide.

Capsule staining is more difficult than other types of differential staining procedures because the capsular materials are water-soluble and may be dislodged and removed with vigorous washing. Smears should not be heated because the resultant cell shrinkage may create a clear zone around the organism that is an artifact that can be mistaken for the capsule.

The capsule stain uses two reagents.

Primary Stain

Crystal Violet (1% aqueous) A violet stain is applied to a non–heat-fixed smear. At this point, the cell and the capsular material will take on the dark color.

Decolorizing Agent and Counterstain

Copper Sulfate (20%) Because the capsule is nonionic, unlike the bacterial cell, the primary stain adheres to the capsule without binding to it. Since the capsule is water-soluble, copper sulfate, rather than water, is used to wash the purple primary stain out of the capsular material without removing the stain that is bound to the cell wall. At the same time, it acts as a counterstain as it is absorbed into the decolorized capsular material. The capsule will now appear light blue in contrast to the deep purple color of the cell.

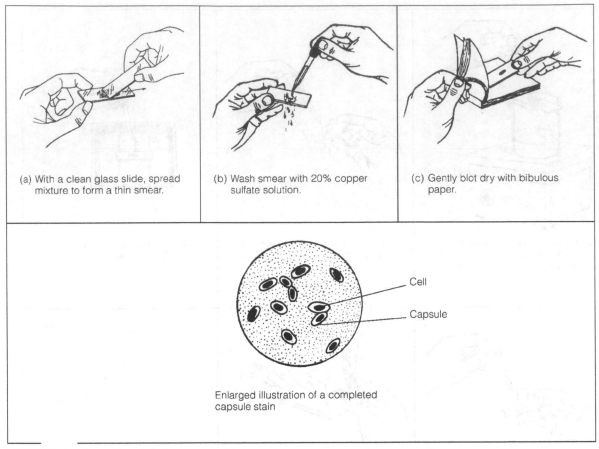

(a) With a clean glass slide, spread mixture to form a thin smear.

(b) Wash smear with 20% copper sulfate solution.

(c) Gently blot dry with bibulous paper.

Cell

Capsule

Enlarged illustration of a completed capsule stain

FIGURE 3 Capsule staining procedure

MATERIALS

Cultures

48-hour-old skimmed milk cultures of *Alcaligenes viscolactis*, *Leuconostoc mesenteroides*, and *Enterobacter aerogenes*.

Reagents

1% crystal violet and 20% copper sulfate ($CuSO_4 \cdot 5H_2O$).

Equipment

Bunsen burner, inoculating loop or needle, staining tray, bibulous paper, lens paper, glass slides, and microscope.

PROCEDURE

The steps are pictured in Figure 3.

1. Obtain one clean glass slide.
2. Place several drops of crystal violet stain on a clean glass slide. Using sterile technique, add three loopfuls of a culture to the stain and **gently** mix with the inoculating loop.
3. With a clean glass slide spread the mixture over the entire surface of the slide to create a very thin smear. Let stand for 5 to 7 minutes.
4. Allow smears to air-dry. **Caution: Do not heat fix.**
5. Wash smears with 20% copper sulfate solution.
6. **Gently** blot dry and examine under oil immersion.
7. Repeat Steps 1 to 6 for each of the remaining test cultures.

Differential Staining for Visualization of Bacterial Cell Structures

Name   Section   Date

OBSERVATIONS AND RESULTS

PART A: Spore Staining Procedure

Following your observation of all slides under oil immersion, record your results in the chart.

1. Make drawings of a representative microscopic field of each preparation.
2. Describe the location of the endospore within the vegetative cell as being central, subterminal, or terminal on each preparation.
3. Indicate color of the spore and vegetative cell on each preparation.

✚ *Refer to the color-plate insert for illustration of this staining procedure.*

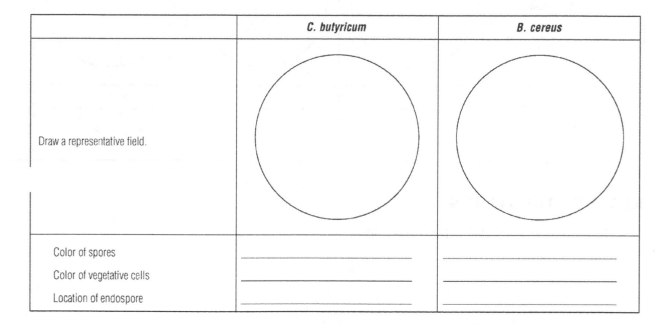

	C. butyricum	*B. cereus*
Draw a representative field.		
Color of spores		
Color of vegetative cells		
Location of endospore		

Differential Staining for Visualization of Bacterial Cell Structures

PART B: Capsule Staining Procedure

Following your observation of all slides under oil immersion, record your results in the chart.

1. Make drawings of a representative microscopic field of each preparation.
2. Record the comparative size of the capsule, that is, small, moderate, or large.
3. Indicate the color of the capsule and the cell on each preparation.

✚ *Refer to the color-plate insert for illustration of this staining procedure.*

	A. viscolactis	L. mesenteroides	E. aerogenes
Draw a representative field.			
Capsule size	_____	_____	_____
Color of capsule	_____	_____	_____
Color of cell	_____	_____	_____

REVIEW QUESTIONS

1. Why is heat necessary in spore staining?

2. Explain the function of water in spore staining.

Differential Staining for Visualization of Bacterial Cell Structures

3. ⟋○ Assume that during the performance of this exercise you made several errors in your spore-staining procedure. In each of the following cases, indicate how your microscopic observations would differ from those observed when the slides were prepared correctly.

a. You used acid-alcohol as the decolorizing agent.

b. You used safranin as the primary stain and malachite green as the counterstain.

c. You did not apply heat during the application of the primary stain.

4. Explain the medical significance of a capsule.

5. Explain the function of copper sulfate in this procedure.

Differential Staining for Visualization of Bacterial Cell Structures

13

Negative Staining

PURPOSE

To perform a negative staining procedure (Figure 1).

PRINCIPLE

Negative staining requires the use of an acidic stain such as India ink or nigrosin. The acidic stain, with its negatively charged chromogen, will not penetrate the cells because of the negative charge on the surface of bacteria. Therefore, the unstained cells are easily discernible against the colored background.

The practical application of negative staining is twofold. First, since heat fixation is not required and the cells are not subjected to the distorting effects of chemicals and heat, their natural size and shape can be seen. Second, it is possible to observe bacteria that are difficult to stain, such as some spirilli.

MATERIALS

Cultures

24-hour agar slant cultures of *Micrococcus luteus*, *Bacillus cereus*, and *Aquaspirillum itersonii*.

Reagent

Nigrosin.

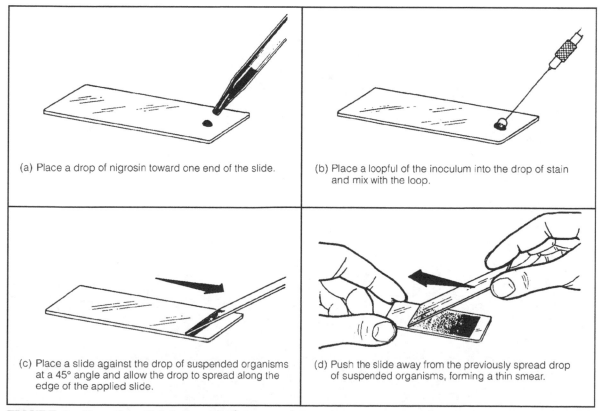

(a) Place a drop of nigrosin toward one end of the slide.

(b) Place a loopful of the inoculum into the drop of stain and mix with the loop.

(c) Place a slide against the drop of suspended organisms at a 45° angle and allow the drop to spread along the edge of the applied slide.

(d) Push the slide away from the previously spread drop of suspended organisms, forming a thin smear.

FIGURE 1   Negative staining procedure

Equipment

Bunsen burner, inoculating loop, staining tray, glass slides, lens paper, and microscope.

PROCEDURE

1. Place a small drop of nigrosin close to one end of a clean slide.

2. Using sterile technique, place a loopful of inoculum from the *M. luteus* culture in the drop of nigrosin and mix.

3. With the edge of a second slide held at a 45° angle and placed in front of the bacterial suspension, push the mixture to form a thin smear.

4. Air-dry. **Do not heat fix the slide**.

5. Repeat Steps 1 to 4 for slide preparations of *Bacillus cereus* and *Aquaspirillum itersonii*.

6. Examine the slides under oil immersion.

Name   Section   Date

OBSERVATIONS AND RESULTS

1. Draw representative fields of your microscopic observations.

✚ *Refer to the color-plate insert for illustration of this staining procedure.*

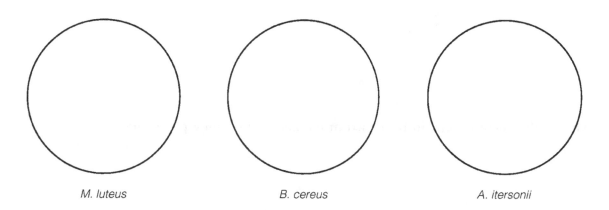

       M. luteus   *B. cereus*   *A. itersonii*

2. Describe the microscopic appearance of the different bacteria.

REVIEW QUESTIONS

1. Can methylene blue be used in place of nigrosin for negative staining? Explain.

2. What are the practical advantages of negative staining?

3. Why do the bacteria remain unstained in the negative staining procedure?

14

MORPHOLOGICAL UNKNOWN TEST
(First Unknown Bacterial Identification Test)

OBJECTIVES

1. To apply skills learned, so far, to characterize unidentified bacterial cultures.
2. Test ability to recognize morphological characteristics of bacteria.
3. Perform and Interpret reactions to differential & structural stains.
4. Report results and submit for grading.

PRINCIPLE

The preliminary steps of bacterial identification use differences in morphology and stain reactions to tell bacteria apart. For this exercise, you will receive slant cultures of bacteria identified only by numbers and letters.

MATERIALS

1. Pure slant cultures of unidentified bacteria a number code, labeled "A" and "B".
2. Inoculating loop, glass slides, and cover glasses.
3. Compound light microscopes.
4. Staining rack and bottles of Staining reagents.

ROCEDURE

1. Personalize your copy of the Morphological Unknown Report sheet with your
   a. Name and Specimen number;
   b. Table number, Seat number, and Lab Day (indicate AM /PM).

2. Refer to your notes or Lab Manual and perform Gram, Acidfast, and Endospore stains on specimens A and B.
3. Use the oil immersion objective lens to observe each slide.
4. Record your observations for each Specimen:

   a. Draw **one** cell to represent the typical shape of each specimen;
   b. Draw between 4 and 8 cells to show how the cells are arranged;
   c. Using (+) or (-) signs only, record Gram, Acidfast, and Endospore stain results.

5. Hand completed report sheet to your instructor for grading. Keep a copy for records.
6. Save all slides until the next class and discard the cultures appropriately.

14

MORPHOLOGICAL UNKNOWN TEST
(First Unknown Bacterial Identification Test)

OBJECTIVES

PRINCIPLE

MATERIALS

PROCEDURE

Morphological Bacteri Identification Sheet
(First Unknown Test)

LAST NAME _____ FIRST NAME _____ DATE _____

LAB DAY/TIME _____ TABLE No. _____ SEAT No. _____

SPECIMEN No.	SHAPE OF CELLS	ARRANGEMENT OF GROUPS OF CELLS	GRAM STAIN	ACIDFAST STAIN	ENDOSPORE STAIN
Unknown Culture A					
Unknown Culture B					

Cultivation of Microorganisms: Nutritional and Physical Requirements, and Enumeration of Microbial Populations

┌─── P U R P O S E S ───┐

To become familiar with

1. The basic nutritional and environmental requirements for the cellular activities of all forms of life.
2. The principles associated with routine and special-purpose media for microbial cultivation.
3. The diversified physical factors essential for microbial cultivation.
4. Specialized techniques for the cultivation of anaerobic microorganisms.
5. The serial dilution–agar plate technique for enumeration of viable microorganisms.
6. The growth dynamics of bacterial populations.

INTRODUCTION

As do all other living organisms, microorganisms require certain basic nutrients and physical factors for the sustenance of life. However, their particular requirements vary greatly. Understanding these needs is necessary for successful cultivation of microorganisms in the laboratory.

Nutritional Needs

Nutritional needs of microbial cells are supplied in the laboratory through a variety of media. The following list illustrates the nutritional diversity that exists among microbes.

1. **Carbon:** This is the most essential and central atom common to all cellular structures and functions. Among microbial cells, two carbon-dependent types are noted:
   a. **Autotrophs:** These organisms can be cultivated in a medium consisting solely of inorganic compounds; specifically, they use inorganic carbon in the form of carbon dioxide.
   b. **Heterotrophs:** These organisms cannot be cultivated in a medium consisting solely of inorganic compounds; they must be supplied with organic nutrients, primarily glucose.

2. **Nitrogen:** This is also an essential atom in many cellular macromolecules, particularly proteins and nucleic acids. Proteins serve as the structural molecules forming the so-called fabric of the cell and as functional molecules, enzymes, that are responsible for the metabolic activities of the cell. Nucleic acids include DNA, the genetic basis of cell life, and RNA, which plays an active role in protein synthesis within the cell. Some microbes use atmospheric nitrogen, others rely on inorganic compounds such as ammonium or nitrate salts, and still others require nitrogen-containing organic compounds such as amino acids.

3. **Nonmetallic elements:** The major nonmetallic ions used for cellular nutrition are
   a. **Sulfur:** This is integral to some amino acids and is therefore a component of proteins. Sources include organic compounds such as sulfur-containing amino acids, inorganic compounds such as sulfates, and elementary sulfur.
   b. **Phosphorus:** This is necessary for the formation of the nucleic acids DNA and RNA and also for synthesis of the high-energy organic compound adenosine triphosphate, ATP. Phosphorus is supplied in the form of phosphate salts for use by all microbial cells.

4. **Metallic elements: Ca^{++}, Zn^{++}, Na^+, K^+, Cu^{++}, Mn^{++}, Mg^{++}, and $Fe^{+2,+3}$** are some of the metallic ions necessary for continued efficient performance of varied cellular activities. Some of these activities are osmoregulation, regulation of enzyme activity, and electron transport during biooxidation. Remember that these ions are micronutrients and are required in trace concentrations only. Inorganic salts supply these materials.

5. **Vitamins:** These organic substances contribute to cellular growth and are essential in minute concentrations for cell activities. They are also sources of coenzymes, which are required for the formation of active enzyme systems. Some microbes require vitamins to be supplied in a preformed state for normal metabolic activities. Some possess extensive vitamin-synthesizing pathways, whereas others can synthesize only a limited number from other compounds present in the medium.

6. **Water:** All cells require water in the medium so that the low-molecular-weight nutrients can cross the cell membrane.

7. **Energy:** Active transport, biosynthesis, and biodegradation of macromolecules are the metabolic activities of cellular life. These activities can be sustained only if there is a constant availability of energy within the cell. Two bioenergetic types of microorganisms exist:
   a. **Phototrophs:** These use radiant energy as their sole energy source.
   b. **Chemotrophs:** These depend on oxidation of chemical compounds as their energy source. Some microbes use organic molecules such as glucose; others utilize inorganic compounds such as H_2S or $NaNO_2$.

Cultivation of Microorganisms

Physical Factors

Three of the most important physical factors that influence the growth and survival of cells are temperature, pH, and the gaseous environment. An understanding of the roles they play in cell metabolism is essential.

1. **Temperature** influences the rate of chemical reactions through its action on cellular enzymes. Bacteria, as a group of organisms, exist over a wide range of temperatures. However, individual species can only exist within a narrower spectrum of temperatures. Low temperatures slow down or inhibit enzyme activity, thereby slowing down or inhibiting cell metabolism and, consequently, cell growth. High temperatures cause coagulation and thus irreversibly denature thermolabile enzymes. Although enzymes differ in their degree of heat sensitivity, generally temperatures in the range of 70°C will destroy most essential enzymes and cause cell death.

2. **The pH of the extracellular environment** greatly affects cells' enzymatic activities. Most commonly, the optimum pH for cell metabolism is in the neutral range of 7. An increase in the hydrogen ion concentration resulting in an acidic pH (below 7) or a decrease in the hydrogen ion concentration resulting in an alkaline pH (above 7) is often detrimental. Either increase or decrease will slow down the rate of chemical reactions because of the destruction of cellular enzymes, thereby affecting the rate of growth and, ultimately, survival.

3. **The gaseous requirement** in most cells is atmospheric oxygen, which is necessary for the biooxidative process of respiration. Atmospheric oxygen plays a vital role in ATP formation and the availability of energy in a utilizable form for cell activities. Other cell types, however, lack the enzyme systems for respiration in the presence of oxygen and therefore must use an anaerobic form of respiration or fermentation.

The following exercises will demonstrate the diversity of nutritional and environmental requirements among microorganisms.

Cultivation of Microorganisms

116

15

The Bacterial Growth Curve

PURPOSES

1. To become familiar with the population growth dynamics of bacterial cultures.
2. To plot a growth curve and determine the generation time of bacterial cultures.

PRINCIPLE

Bacterial population growth studies require inoculation of viable cells into a sterile broth medium and incubation of the culture under optimum temperature, pH, and gaseous conditions. Under these conditions, the cells will reproduce rapidly and the dynamics of the microbial growth can be charted by means of a population growth curve, which is constructed by plotting the increase cell numbers versus time of incubation. The curve can be used to delineate stages of the growth cycle. It also facilitates measurement of cell numbers and the rate of growth of a particular organism under standardized conditions as expressed by its **generation time**, the time required for a microbial population to double.

The stages of a typical growth curve (Figure 1) are

1. **Lag phase:** During this stage the cells are adjusting to their new environment. Cellular metabolism is accelerated, resulting in rapid biosynthesis of cellular macromolecules, primarily enzymes, in preparation for the next phase of the cycle. Although the cells are increasing in size, there is no cell division and therefore no increase in numbers.

2. **Logarithmic (log) phase:** Under optimum nutritional and physical conditions, the physiologically robust cells reproduce at a uniform and rapid rate by binary fission. Thus there is a rapid exponential increase in population, which doubles regularly until a maximum number of cells is reached. The time required for

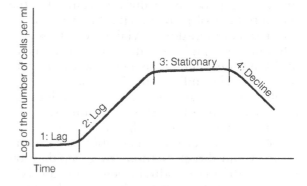

FIGURE 1 Population growth curve

the population to double is the generation time. The length of the log phase varies, depending on the organisms and the composition of the medium. The average may be estimated to last 6 to 12 hours.

3. **Stationary phase:** During this stage, the number of cells undergoing division is equal to the number of cells that are dying. Therefore there is no further increase in cell number, and the population is maintained at its maximum level for a period of time. The primary factors responsible for this phase are the depletion of some essential metabolites and the accumulation of toxic acidic or alkaline end products in the medium.

4. **Decline, or death, phase:** Because of the continuing depletion of nutrients and buildup of metabolic wastes, the microorganisms die at a rapid and uniform rate. The decrease in population closely parallels its increase during the log phase. Theoretically, the entire population should die during a time interval equal to that of the log phase. This does not occur, however, since a small number of highly resistant organisms persist for an indeterminate length of time.

Construction of a complete bacterial growth curve requires that aliquots of a 24-hour shake-flask culture be measured for population size at intervals during the incubation period. Such a procedure does not lend itself to a regular laboratory session. Therefore this experiment follows a modified procedure designed to demonstrate only the lag and log phases. The curve will be plotted on semilog paper by using two values for the measurement of growth. The direct method requires enumeration of viable cells in serially diluted samples of the test culture taken at 30-minute intervals as described in Experiment 19. The indirect method uses spectrophotometric measurement of the developing turbidity at the same 30-minute intervals, as an index of increasing cellular mass.

You will determine generation time with indirect and direct methods by using data on the growth curve. Indirect determination is made by simple extrapolation from the log phase as illustrated in Figure 2. Select two points on the optical density scale, such as 0.2 and 0.4, that represent a doubling of turbidity. Using a ruler, extrapolate by drawing a line between each of the selected optical densit⁻⁻ on the ordinate (x-axis) and the plotte of the growth curve. Then draw perpendicular lines from these end points on the plotted line of the growth curve to their respective time intervals on the abscissa (y-axis). With this information, determine the generation time as follows:

$$GT = t_{(O.D.\ 0.4)} - t_{(O.D.\ 0.2)}$$

GT = 90 minutes − 60 minutes = 30 minutes

The direct method uses the log of cell number scale on the growth curve and the following formula:

$$GT = \frac{t \log 2}{\log b - \log B}$$

GT = generation time;
B = number of bacterial cells at some point during the log phase;
b = number of bacterial cells at a second point of the log phase;
t = time in hours or minutes between B and b.

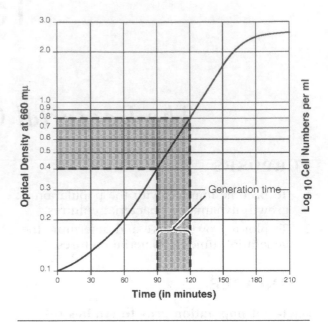

FIGURE 2 **Indirect method of determining generation time**

MATERIALS

Cultures

5–10-hour (log phase) brain–heart infusion broth culture of *Escherichia coli* with O.D. of 0.08–0.10 at 600 mμ.

Media

Per designated student group: 100 ml of brain–heart infusion in a 250-ml Erlenmeyer flask; 18 99-ml sterile water blanks; and four 100-ml bottles of nutrient agar.

Equipment

37°C waterbath shaker incubator, Bausch & Lomb Spectronic 20 spectrophotometer, 13 × 100 mm cuvettes, Quebec colony counter, 24 sterile Petri dishes, 1-ml and 10-ml sterile pipettes, mechanical pipetting device, glassware marking pencil, 1000-ml beaker, and Bunsen burner.

PROCEDURE

1. Separate the 18 99-ml sterile water blanks into six sets of three water blanks each. Label each set as to time of inoculation (t_0, t_{30}, t_{60}, t_{90}, t_{120}, t_{150}) and the dilution to be effected in each water blank (10^{-2}, 10^{-4}, 10^{-6}).

2. Label six sets of four Petri dishes as to time of inoculation and dilution to be plated (10^{-4}, 10^{-5}, 10^{-6}, 10^{-7}).

3. Liquefy the four bottles of nutrient agar in an autoclave. Cool and maintain at 45°C.

4. With a sterile pipette, add approximately 5 ml of the log phase *E. coli* culture to the flask containing 100 ml of brain–heart infusion broth. The approximate initial O.D. (t_0) should be 0.08 to 0.1 at 600 mμ. Refer to Experiment 13 for proper use of the spectrophotometer.

5. After the t_0 O.D. has been determined, shake the culture flask and aseptically transfer 1 ml to the 99-ml water blank labeled t_0 10^{-2} and continue to dilute serially to 10^{-4} and 10^{-6}. **A new pipette must be used for each subsequent dilution.**

6. Place the culture flask in a waterbath shaker set at 120 rpm at 37°C, and time for the required 30-minute intervals.

7. Shake the t_0 dilution bottle as illustrated in Figure 3. Plate the t_0 dilutions on the appropriately labeled t_0 plates as shown in Figure 4. Aseptically pour 15 ml of the molten agar into each plate and mix by gentle rotation.

FIGURE 3 Method for mixing sample in a dilution bottle

8. Thereafter, at each 30-minute interval, shake and aseptically transfer a 5-ml aliquot of the culture to a cuvette and determine its optical density. Also, aseptically transfer a 1-ml aliquot of the culture into the 10^{-2} water blank of the set labeled with the appropriate time, complete the serial dilution, and plate in the respectively labeled Petri dishes. **A new pipette must be used for each subsequent dilution.**

9. When the pour-plate cultures harden, incubate them in an inverted position for 24 hours at 37°C.

The Bacterial Growth Curve

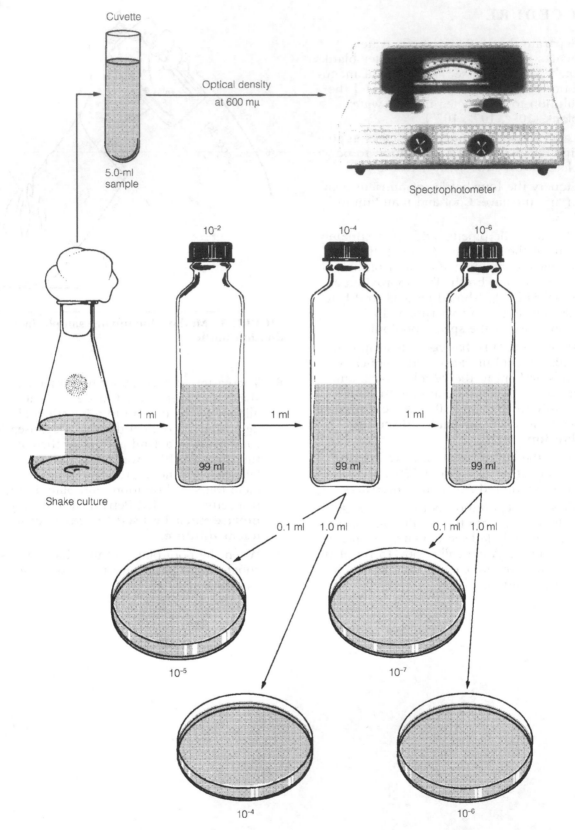

FIGURE 4 Spectrophotometric and dilution-plating procedure for use in bacterial growth curves

The Bacterial Growth Curve

Name   Section   Date

OBSERVATIONS AND RESULTS

1. Perform cell counts on all plates. Cell counts are often referred to as colony-forming units (CFUs) because each single cell in the plate becomes visible as a colony, which can then be counted.
2. Record the optical densities and corresponding cell counts in the chart.

Incubation Time (minutes)	Optical Density @ 600 mμ	Plate Counts (CFU/ml)	Log of CFU/ml
0			
30			
60			
90			
120			
150			

3. On the provided semilog paper:
   a. Plot a curve relating the optical densities on the ordinate versus incubation time on the abscissa as shown in Figure 2
   b. Plot a population curve with the log of the viable cells/ml on the ordinate and the incubation time on the abscissa. On both graphs, use a ruler to draw the best line connecting the plotted points. The straight-line portion of the curve represents the log phase.
4. Calculate the generation time for this culture by the direct method (using the mathematical formula) and by the indirect method (extrapolating from the O.D. scale on the plotted curve). Show calculations, and record the generation time.

Generation Time

Direct method:

Indirect method:

The Bacterial Growth Curve

REVIEW QUESTIONS

1. Does the term *growth* convey the same meaning when applied to bacteria and to multicellular organisms? Explain.

2. Why do variations in generation time exist:

    a. Among different species of microorganisms?

    b. Within a single microbial species?

3. 🔍 The generation time and growth rate of an organism grown in the laboratory can be ea   etermined by constructing a typical growth curve.

    a. Would you expect the growth rate of the infectious organisms found in an abscess that developed from a wound to mimic the growth curve obtained in the laboratory? Explain.

    b. Would you expect antibiotic therapy to be effective without any other concurrent treatment of the abscess?

4. 🔍 Is generation time a useful parameter to indicate the types of media best suited to support the growth of a specific organism? Explain.

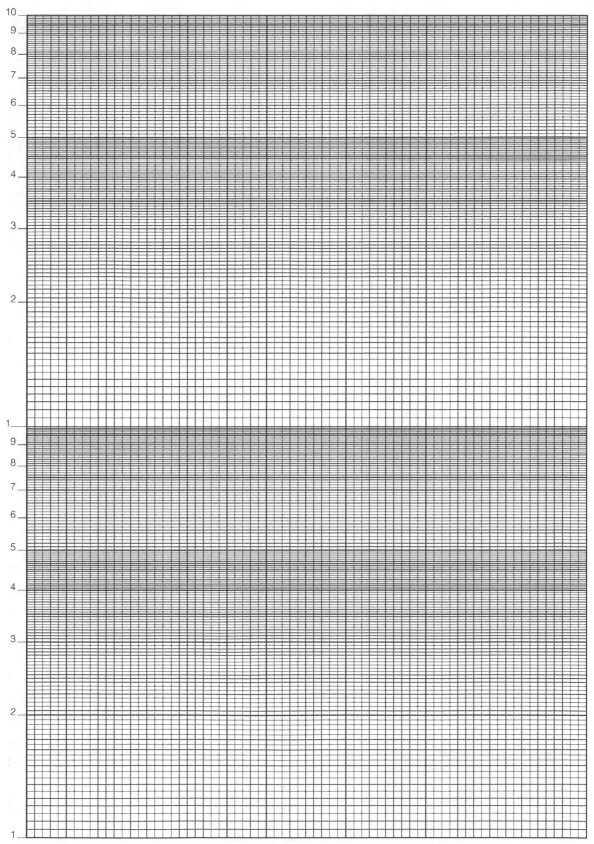

Optical Density versus Incubation Time

The Bacterial Growth Curve

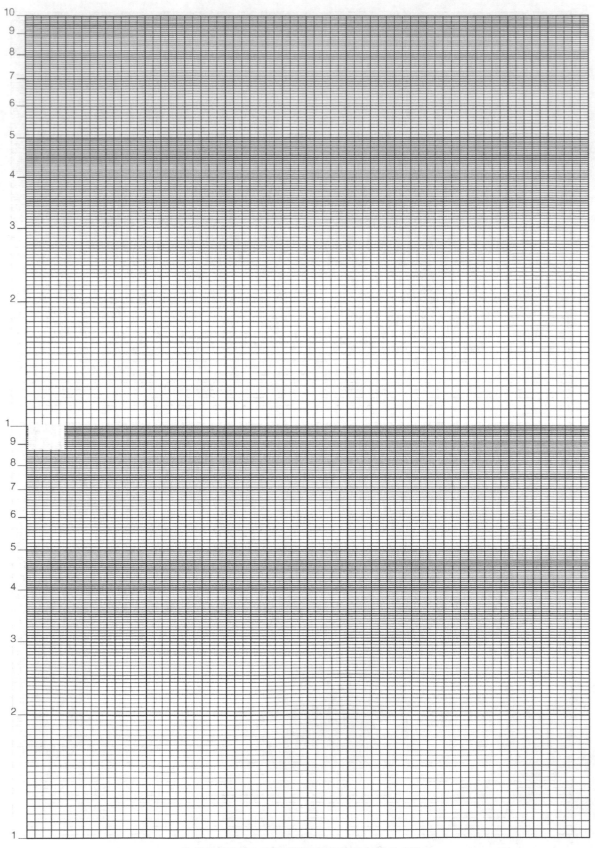

Colony Forming Units (CFUs) versus Incubation Time

The Bacterial Growth Curve

Use of the Spectrophotometer

In a **spectrophotometer,** a beam of light is transmitted through a bacterial suspension to a photoelectric cell (Figure 1). As bacterial numbers increase, the broth becomes more turbid, causing the light to scatter and allowing less light to reach the photoelectric cell. The change in light is registered on the instrument as **percentage of transmission,** or **%T** (the amount of light getting through the suspension) and **absorbance (Abs.)** (a value derived from the percentage of transmission). Absorbance is a logarithmic value and is used to plot bacterial growth on a graph.

Operation of the Spectronic 20 and Meter-Model Spectronic 21 Spectrophotometers (Figure 2)

1. Turn on the power and allow the instrument to warm up for 15 minutes.
   Set the wavelength for maximum absorption of the bacteria and minimal absorption of the culture medium.

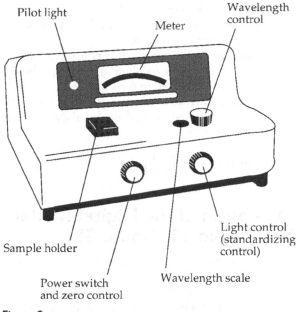

Figure 2
Bausch and Lomb Spectronic 20.

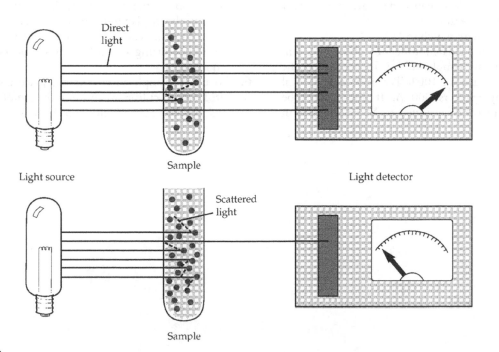

Figure 1
Estimation of bacterial numbers by turbidity. The amount of light picked up by the light detector is proportional to the number of bacteria. The less light transmitted, the more bacteria in the sample.

3. For the Spectronic 20, *zero* the instrument by turning the zero control until the needle measures 0% transmission.

4. To read a metered scale, look directly at the meter so the needle is superimposed on its reflection in the mirror.

5. Place an uninoculated tube of culture medium (*control*) in the sample holder. To *standardize* the instrument, turn the light control until the needle registers 100% transmission.

6. To take a sample measurement, place an inoculated tube of culture medium in the sample holder and record the %T from the scale.

7. %T is usually read on the Spectronic 20 because it is the more accurate scale. Calculate the absorbance as follows:

$$\text{Absorbance} = -\log\left(\frac{\%T}{100}\right)$$

Operation of the Digital-Model Spectronic 21 (Figure 3)

1. Turn on the power and allow the instrument to warm up for 15 minutes.

2. Set the wavelength for maximum absorption of the bacteria and minimal absorption of the culture medium.

3. Select the operating mode: A (absorbance) or %T (transmission). Absorbance data are more linear and usually preferable.

4. Set the sensitivity switch to LO.

5. Place an uninoculated tube of culture medium (*control*) in the sample holder. To *standardize* the instrument, turn the 100% T/Zero A control until the display registers 000 A. If 000 A can't be reached, turn the sensitivity to M or HI. A U in

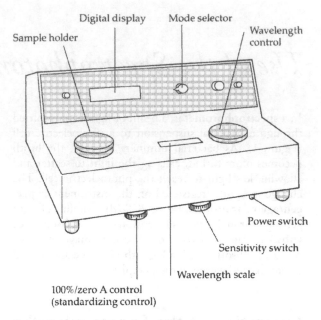

Figure 3
Bausch and Lomb Spectronic 21, digital model.

the upper-left corner of the display indicates that you are under the range of the light detector, and an O in the display indicates that you are over the range. In either case, use the sensitivity switch and the standardizing control to make the necessary adjustments.

6. To take a sample measurement, place an inoculated tube of culture medium in the sample holder and record the absorbance (Abs.) from the display.

Physical and Chemical Agents for the Control of Microbial Growth

PURPOSES

1. To become acquainted with the basic methods for inhibiting microbial growth and their modes of antimicrobial action.
2. To demonstrate the effects of physical agents, moist heat, osmotic pressure, and ultraviolet radiation on selected microbial populations.
3. To demonstrate effects on selected microbial populations of chemical agents used as disinfectants, antiseptics, and antibiotics.

INTRODUCTION

Control of microorganisms is essential in the home, industry, and medical fields to prevent and treat diseases and to inhibit the spoilage of foods and other industrial products. Common methods of control involve chemical and physical agents that adversely affect microbial structures and functions, thereby producing a microbicidal or microbistatic effect. A **microbicidal effect** is one that kills the microbes immediately; a **microbistatic effect** inhibits the reproductive capacities of the cells and maintains the microbial population at a constant size.

Chemical Methods for Control of Microbial Growth

1. **Antiseptics:** Chemical substances used on living tissue that kill or inhibit the growth of vegetative microbial forms.
2. **Disinfectants:** Chemical substances that kill or inhibit the growth of vegetative microbial forms on nonliving materials.
3. **Chemotherapeutic agents:** Chemical substances that destroy or inhibit the growth of microorganisms in living tissues.

Physical Methods for Control of Microbial Growth

The modes of action of the different chemical and physical agents of control vary, although they all produce damaging effects to one or more essential cellular structures or molecules in order to cause cell death or inhibition of growth. Sites of damage that can result in malfunction are the cell wall, cell membrane, cytoplasm, enzymes, or nucleic acids. The adverse effects manifest themselves in the following ways.

128

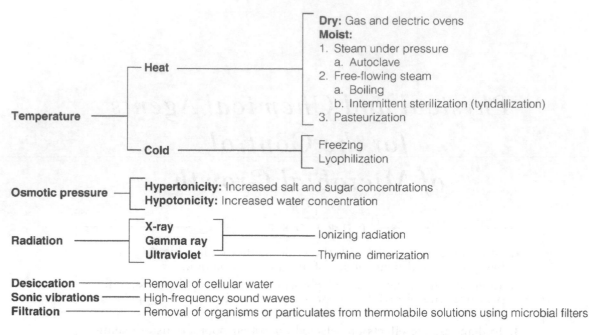

FIGURE 1   **Physical methods used for the control of microbial growth**

1. **Cell-wall injury:** This can result in one of two ways. First, lysis of the cell wall will leave the protoplast susceptible to osmotic damage, and a hypotonic environment may cause lysis of the vulnerable protoplast. Second, certain agents inhibit cell wall synthesis, which is essential during microbial cell reproduction. Failure to synthesize a missing segment of the cell wall results in an unprotected protoplast.

2. **Cell-membrane damage:** This may be the result of lysis of the membrane, which will cause immediate cell death. Also, the selective nature of the membrane may be affected without causing its complete disruption. As a result, there may be a loss of essential cellular molecules or interference with the uptake of nutrients. In both cases, metabolic processes will be adversely affected.

3. **Alteration of the colloidal state of cytoplasm:** Certain agents cause denaturing of cytoplasmic proteins. If this occurs, it will produce irreversible cell damage. Uncoiling of these macromolecules leads to coagulation of the proteins, which in their clumped state are biologically inactive.

4. **Inactivation of enzymes:** When this results from the activity of certain physical and chemical agents, the cell cannot perform essential life functions. Inactivation of enzymes by these agents occurs through the mechanisms of competitive or noncompetitive inhibition, which will be discussed in a later exercise.

5. **Interference with the structure and function of the DNA molecule:** The DNA molecule is the control center of the cell and may also represent a cellular target area for destruction or inhibition. Some agents have an affinity for DNA and cause breakage or distortion of the molecule, thereby interfering with its replication and role in protein synthesis.

Physical and Chemical Agents for the Control of Microbial Growth

Figure 1 illustrates the acceptable physical methods used for the control of microbial growth.

Awareness of the mode of action of the physical and chemical agents is absolutely essential for their proper selection and application in microbial control. The exercises in this section are designed to acquaint you more fully with several commonly employed agents and their uses.

130

16

Chemical Agents of Control: Chemotherapeutic Agents

Chemotherapeutic agents are chemical substances used in the treatment of infectious diseases. Their mode of action is to interfere with microbial metabolism, thereby producing a bacteriostatic or bacteriocidal effect on the microorganisms, without producing a like effect in host cells. These drugs can be separated into two categories:

1. **Antibiotics** are synthesized and secreted by some true bacteria, actinomycetes, and fungi that destroy or inhibit the growth of other microorganisms. Today, some antibiotics are laboratory synthesized or modified; however, their origins are living cells.

   Synthetic drugs are synthesized in the laboratory.

To determine a therapeutic drug of choice, one must know its mode of action, possible adverse side effects in the host, and the scope of its antimicrobial activity. The specific mechanism of action varies among different drugs, and the short-term or long-term use of many drugs can produce systemic side effects in the host. These vary in severity from mild and temporary upsets to permanent tissue damage (Table 1).

SYNTHETIC AGENTS

Sulfadiazine (a sulfonamide) produces a static effect on a wide range of microorganisms by a mechanism of action called **competitive inhibition**. The active component of the drug, sulfanilamide, acts as an **antimetabolite** that competes with the **essential metabolite**, *p*-aminobenzoic acid (PABA), during the synthesis of folic acid in the microbial cell. Folic acid is an essential cellular coenzyme involved in the synthesis of amino acids and purines. Many microorganisms possess enzymatic pathways for folic acid synthesis and can be adversely affected by sulfonamides. Human cells lack these enzymes, and the essential folic acid

TABLE 1 Prototypic Antibiotics

Antibiotic	Mode of Action	Possible Side Effects
Penicillin	Prevents transpeptidation of the N-acetylmuramic acids, producing a weakened peptidoglycan structure	Penicillin resistance; sensitivity (allergic reaction)
Streptomycin	Has an affinity for bacterial ribosomes, causing misreading of codons on mRNA, hereby interfering with protein synthesis	May produce damage to auditory nerve, causing deafness
Chloramphenicol	Has an affinity for bacterial ribosomes, preventing peptide bond formation between amino acids during protein synthesis	May cause aplastic anemia, which is fatal because of destruction of RBC-forming and WBC-forming tissues
Tetracyclines	Have an affinity for bacterial ribosomes; prevent hydrogen bonding between the anticodon on the tRNA–amino acid complex and the codon on mRNA during protein synthesis	Permanent discoloration of teeth in young children
Bacitracin	Inhibits cell-wall synthesis	Nephrotoxic if taken internally; used for topical application only
Polymyxin	Destruction of cell membrane	Toxic if taken internally; used for topical application only

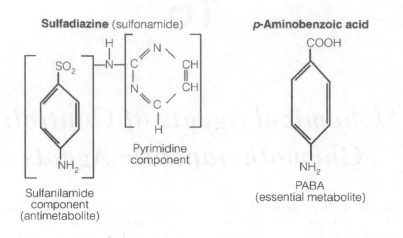

Sulfadiazine (sulfonamide)

SO_2

NH_2

Sulfanilamide
component
(antimetabolite)

Pyrimidine
component

p-Aminobenzoic acid

COOH

NH_2

PABA
(essential metabolite)

FIGURE 1   Chemical similarity of sulfanilamide and PABA

enters the cells in a preformed state. There-fore these drugs have no competitive effect on human cells. The similarity between the chemical structure of the antimetabolite sul-fanilamide and the structure of the essential metabolite PABA is illustrated in Figure 1.

PART A: The Kirby-Bauer Anti   ic Sensitivity Test Procedure

PURPOSE

To become acquainted with the Kirby-Bauer procedure for the evaluation of the antimi-crobial activity of chemotherapeutic agents.

PRINCIPLE

The available chemotherapeutic agents vary in their scope of antimicrobial activity. Some have a limited spectrum of activity, being effective against only one group of micro-organisms. Others exhibit broad-spectrum activity against a range of microorganisms. The drug susceptibilities of many pathogenic microorganisms are known, but it is some-times necessary to test several agents to de-termine the drug of choice.

A standardized filter-paper disc–agar dif-fusion procedure, known as the Kirby-Bauer method, is frequently used to determine the drug susceptibility of microorganisms iso-lated from infectious processes (Figure 2). This method allows the rapid determination of the efficacy of a drug by measuring the

diameter of the zone of inhibition that re-sults from diffusion of the agent into the medium surrounding the disc. In this proce-dure, filter-paper discs of uniform size are impregnated with specified concentrations of different antibiotics and then placed on the surface of an agar plate that has been seeded with the organism to be tested. The medium of choice is Mueller-Hinton agar, with a pH of 7.2 to 7.4, which is poured into plates to a uniform depth of 5 mm and refrigerated on solidification. Prior to use, the plates are transferred to an incubator at 37°C for 10 to 20 minutes to dry off the moisture that de-velops on the agar surface. The plates are then heavily inoculated with a standardized inoculum by means of a cotton swab to en-sure the confluent growth of the organism. The discs are aseptically applied to the sur-face of the agar plate at well-spaced inter-vals. Once applied, each disc is gently touched with a sterile applicator stick to ensure its firm contact with the agar surface.

Following incubation, the plates are ex-amined for the presence of growth inhibi-tion, which is indicated by a clear zone sur-rounding each disc. The susceptibility of an organism to a drug is determined by the size of this zone, which itself is dependent on variables such as:

1. The ability and rate of diffusion of the antibiotic into the medium and its inter-action with the test organism.
2. The number of organisms inoculated.
3. The growth rate of the organism.
4. The degree of susceptibility of the organ-ism to the antibiotic.

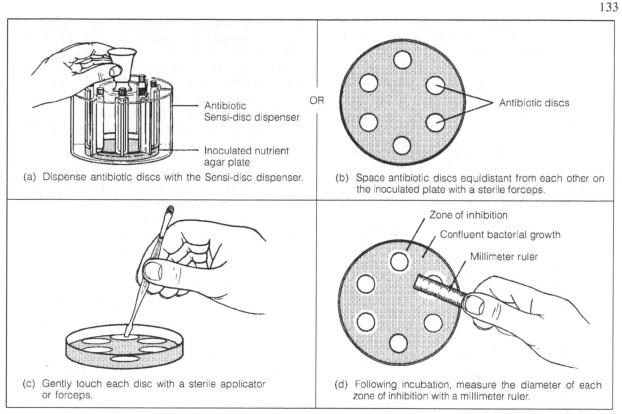

(a) Dispense antibiotic discs with the Sensi-disc dispenser.

Antibiotic
Sensi-disc dispenser

Inoculated nutrient
agar plate

OR

(b) Space antibiotic discs equidistant from each other on the inoculated plate with a sterile forceps.

Antibiotic discs

(c) Gently touch each disc with a sterile applicator or forceps.

Zone of inhibition
Confluent bacterial growth
Millimeter ruler

(d) Following incubation, measure the diameter of each zone of inhibition with a millimeter ruler.

FIGURE 2 Kirby-Bauer antibiotic sensitivity procedure

A measurement of the diameter of the zone of inhibition in millimeters is made, and its size is compared to that contained in a standardized chart, which is shown in Table 2. Based on this comparison, the test organism is determined to be resistant, intermediate, or susceptible to the antibiotic.

MATERIALS

Cultures

0.85% saline suspensions of *Escherichia coli*, *Staphylococcus aureus*, *Pseudomonas aeruginosa*, *Proteus vulgaris*, *Mycobacterium smegmatis*, *Bacillus cereus*, and *Enterococcus faecalis* adjusted to an O.D. of 0.1 at 600 mμ. **Note:** For enhanced growth of *M. smegmatis*, add Tween 80 (1 ml/liter broth medium) and incubate for 3 to 5 days in a shaking waterbath, if available.

Media

Per designated student group: seven Mueller-Hinton agar plates.

Antimicrobial Sensitivity Discs

Penicillin G, 10 μg; streptomycin, 10 μg; tetracycline, 30 μg; chloramphenicol, 30 μg; gentamicin, 10 μg; vancomycin, 30 μg; and sulfanilamide, 300 μg.

Equipment

Sensi-disc™ dispensers or forceps, Bunsen burner, sterile cotton swabs, glassware marking pencil, and millimeter ruler.

PROCEDURE

1. Place agar plates right side up in an incubator heated to 37°C for 10 to 20 minutes with the covers adjusted so that the plates are slightly opened.
2. Label the covers of each of the plates with the name of the test organism to be inoculated.
3. Using sterile technique, inoculate all agar plates with their respective test organisms as follows:
   a. Dip a sterile cotton swab into a well-mixed saline test culture and remove

134

excess inoculum by pressing the saturated swab against the inner wall of the culture tube.

b. Using the swab, streak the entire agar surface horizontally, vertically, and around the outer edge of the plate to ensure a heavy growth over the entire surface.

4. Allow all culture plates to dry for about 5 minutes.

5. Using the Sensi-disc dispenser, apply the antibiotic discs by placing the dispenser over the agar surface and pressing the plunger, depositing the discs simultaneously onto the agar surface. If dispensers are not available, distribute the individual discs at equal distances with forceps dipped in alcohol and flamed.

6. Gently press each disc down with the wooden end of a cotton swab or sterile forceps to ensure that the discs adhere to the surface of the agar. **Do not press the discs into the agar.**

7. Incubate all plate cultures in an inverted position for 24 to 48 hours at 37°C.

PART B: Synergistic Effect of Drug Combinations

PURPOSE

To become acquainted with the disc–agar diffusion technique for determination of synergistic combinations of chemotherapeutic agents.

PRINCIPLE

Combination chemotherapy, the use of two or more antimicrobial or antineoplastic agents, is being employed in medical practice with ever-increasing frequency. The rationale for using drug combinations is the expectation that effective combinations might lower the incidence of bacterial resistance, reduce host toxicity of the antimicrobial agents (because of decreased dosage requirements), or enhance the agents' bactericidal activity. Enhanced bactericidal activity is known as **synergism**. Synergistic activity is evident when the sum of the effects of the

chemotherapeutic agents used in combination is significantly greater than the sum of their effects when used individually. This result is readily differentiated from an **additive (indifferent) effect**, which is evident when the interaction of two drugs produces a combined effect that is no greater than the sum of their separately measured individual effects.

A variety of *in vitro* methods are available to demonstrate synergistic activity. In this experiment, a disc–agar diffusion technique will be performed to demonstrate this phenomenon. This technique uses the Kirby-Bauer antibiotic susceptibility test procedure, as described in Part A of this experiment, and requires both Mueller-Hinton agar plates previously seeded with the test organisms and commercially prepared, antimicrobial-impregnated discs. The two discs, representing the drug combination, are placed on the inoculated agar plate and separated by a distance (measured in mm) that is equal to or slightly greater than one-half the sum of their individual zones of inhibition when obtained separately. Following the incubation period, an additive effect is exhibited by the presence of two distinctly separate circles of inhibition. If the drug combination is synergistic, the two inhibitory zones merge to form a "bridge" at their juncture, as illustrated in Figure 3.

The drug combinations to be used in this experimental procedure are:

1. **Sulfisoxazole, 150 μg**, and **trimethoprim, 5 μg.** Both antimicrobial agents are enzyme inhibitors that act sequentially in the metabolic pathway leading to folic acid synthesis. The antimicrobial effect of each drug is enhanced when the two drugs are used in combination. The pathway thus exemplifies synergism.

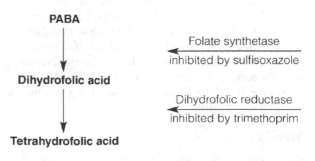

Chemical Agents of Control: Chemotherapeutic Agents

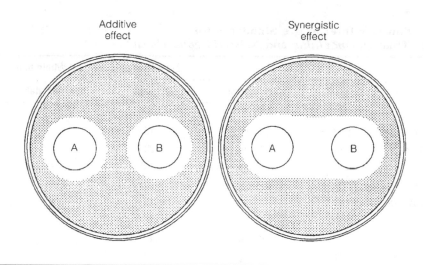

FIGURE 3 **Additive and synergistic effects of drug combinations**

2. **Trimethoprim, 5 μg,** and **tetracycline, 30 μg.** The modes of antimicrobial activity of these two chemotherapeutic agents differ; tetracycline acts to interfere with protein synthesis at the ribosomes. Thus, when used in combination, these drugs produce an additive effect.

ATERIALS

Cultures

0.85% saline suspensions of *Escherichia coli* and *Staphylococcus aureus* adjusted to an O.D. of 0.1 at 600 mμ.

Media

Per designated student group: four Mueller-Hinton agar plates.

Antimicrobial-Sensitivity Discs

Tetracycline, 30 μg; trimethoprim, 5 μg; and sulfisoxazole, 150 μg.

Equipment

Bunsen burner, forceps, sterile cotton swabs, millimeter ruler, and glassware marking pencil.

PROCEDURE

1. Inoculation of Mueller-Hinton agar plates: Follow Steps 1 through 4 as described under the procedure in Part A of this experiment.

2. Using the millimeter ruler, determine the center of the underside of each plate and mark with a glassware marking pencil.

3. Using the glassware marking pencil, mark the underside of each agar plate culture at both sides from the center mark at the distances specified below:

   a. *E. coli*–inoculated plate for trimethoprim and sulfisoxazole combination sensitivity: 12.5 mm on each side of center mark.

   b. *S. aureus*–inoculated plate for trimethoprim and sulfisoxazole combination sensitivity: 14.5 mm on each side of center mark.

   c. *E. coli*– and *S. aureus*–inoculated plates for trimethoprim and tetracycline combination sensitivity: 14.0 mm on each side of center mark.

4. Using sterile forceps, place the antimicrobial discs, in the combinations specified in step 3, onto the surface of each agar plate culture at the previously marked positions. Gently press each disc down with the sterile forceps to ensure that it adheres to the agar surface.

5. Incubate all plate cultures in an inverted position for 24 to 48 hours at 37°C.

TABLE 2 Zone Diameter Interpretive Standards for Organisms Other Than *Haemophilus* and *Neisseria gonorrhoea*

Antimicrobial Agent	Disk Content	Zone Diameter, Nearest Whole mm		
		Resistant	Intermediate[k]	Susceptible
Ampicillin[a]				
when testing gram-negative enteric organisms	10 μg	≤ 13	—	≥ 17
when testing staphylococci[b]	10 μg	≤ 28	—	≥ 29
when testing enterococci[c]	10 μg	≤ 16	—	—
when testing non-enterococcal streptococci[c]	10 μg	≤ 21	—	≥ 30
when testing *Listeria monocytogenes*	10 μg	≤ 19	—	≥ 20
Carbenicillin[b]				
when testing *Pseudomonas*	100 μg	≤ 13	—	≥ 17
when testing other gram-negative organisms	100 μg	≤ 19	—	≥ 23
Cefoxitin[d]	30 μg	≤ 14	—	≥ 18
Cephalothin[d]	30 μg	≤ 14	—	≥ 18
Chloramphenicol	30 μg	≤ 12	13–17	≥ 18
Clindamycin[a]	2 μg	≤ 14	15–20	≥ 21
Erythromycin	15 μg	≤ 13	14–22	≥ 23
Gentamicin[e]	10 μg	≤ 12	13–14	≥ 15
Kanamycin	30 μg	≤ 13	14–17	≥ 18
Methicillin when testing staphylococci[f]	5 μg	≤ 9	10–13	≥ 14
Novobiocin[g]	30 μg	≤ 17	18–21	≥ 22
Penicillin G				
when taphylococci[b]	10 units	≤ 28	—	≥ 29
when testing enterococci[c]	10 units	≤ 14	—	—
when testing *L. monocytogenes*	10 units	≤ 19	—	≥ 20
when testing non-enterococcal streptococci	10 units	≤ 19	—	≥ 28
Rifampin	5 μg	≤ 16	17–19	≥ 20
Streptomycin	10 μg	≤ 11	12–14	≥ 15
Tetracycline[h]	30 μg	≤ 14	15–18	≥ 19
Tobramycin[e]	10 μg	≤ 12	13–14	≥ 15
Trimethoprim/sulfamethoxazole[i]	1.25/23.75 μg	≤ 10	—	≥ 16
Vancomycin				
when testing enterococci	30 μg	≤ 9	10–11	—
when testing other gram-positives	30 μg	≤ 9	10–11	≥ 12
Urinary Tract Specific Antimicrobial Agents[j]				
Sulfonamides[i]	250 or 300 μg	≤ 12	—	≥ 17
Trimethoprim[i]	5 μg	≤ 10	—	≥ 16

Permission to excerpt portions of M2-A4 (Performance Standards for Antimicrobial Disk Susceptibility Tests—Fourth Edition; Approved Standard) has been granted by NCCLS. The interpretive data are valid only if the methodology in M2-A4 is followed. NCCLS frequently updates the interpretive tables through new editions of the standards and supplements to them. Users should refer to the most recent editions. The current standard may be obtained from NCCLS, 940 West Valley Road, Suite 1400, Wayne, PA 19087, U.S.A.

[a]The clindamycin disk is used for testing susceptibility to both clindamycin and lincomycin.

[b]Resistant strains of *S. aureus* produce ß-lactamase and the testing of the 10-unit *penicillin G disk is preferred.* Penicillin G should be used to test the susceptibility of all penicillinase-sensitive penicillins, such as ampicillin, amoxicillin, azlocillin, bacampicillin, carbenicillin, hetacillin, mezlocillin, piperacillin,

and ticarcillin. Results may also be applied to phenoxymethyl penicillin or phenethicillin.

[c]For enterococci, aerococci, and non-enterococcal streptococci, the designation "moderately susceptible" implies the need for high-dose penicillin or ampicillin for endocarditis and serious invasive tissue infections that may require (always for enterococci) combined therapy with an aminoglycoside (gentamicin) for

Chemical Agents of Control: Chemotherapeutic Agents

improved therapeutic response and bactericidal action. Non-enterococcal strep-tococci should have an MIC determined in case of endocarditis. Urinary iso-lates should be considered to be susceptible to ampicillin or penicillin alone.

[d]Ampicillin/sulbactam, aztreonam, cefotetan, ceftazidime, ceftriaxone, and imipenem are among the most recently studied ß-lactams having a separate diagnostic disk and a generally wider spectrum of antimicrobial activity, espe-cially against gram-negative bacilli when compared to previously approved cephalosporins such as cephalothin. **The 30-µg Cefazolin test results may not accurately predict susceptibility to other first-generation cephalosporins. Cephalothin should be tested instead to represent cephalothin, cefaclor (except for *Haemophilus*), cephapirin, cephra-dine, cephalexin, and cefadroxil.** *S. aureus strains exhibiting resistance to one of the penicillinase-resistant penicillins (MRSA) must be reported as resistant to cephalosporins and other newer ß-lactams such as amoxicillin/ clavulanic acid, ampicillin/sulbactam, imipenem and ticarcillin/clavulanic acid, regardless of in vitro test results.* This is primarily because in most cases of documented MRSA infection, the patient has responded poorly to the cephalo-sporin therapy or convincing clinical data has yet to be derived confirming clinical efficacy (clavulanic acid or sulbactam combinations and imipenem). Methicillin-resistant, coagulase-negative *Staphylococcus* spp. also appear *not* to respond well to the above cited drugs.

[e]The zone sizes obtained with aminoglycosides, particularly when testing *P. aeruginosa*, are very medium-dependent because of variations in divalent cation content. These interpretive standards are to be used only with Mueller-Hinton medium that has yielded zone diameters within the correct range shown when performance tests were done with *P. aeruginosa* ATCC® 27853. Organ-isms in the intermediate category may be either susceptible or resistant when tested by dilution methods and should therefore more properly be classified as "indeterminate" in their susceptibility.

[f]Of the antistaphylococcal, ß-lactamase-resistant penicillins, either oxacillin or methicillin could be tested, and results can be applied to the other two of these drugs and to cloxacillin and dicloxacillin. *Oxacillin is preferred* due to more resistance to degradation in storage and its application to pneumococcal testing and because it is more likely to detect heteroresistant staphylococcal strains. Do not use nafcillin on blood-containing media. Cloxacillin disks should not be used, because they may not detect methicillin-resistant *S. aureus*. When intermediate results are obtained with staphylococci, the strains should be further investigated to determine if they are heteroresistant.

[g]Data on novobiocin **are not** based on the NCCLS standard.

[h]Tetracycline is the class disk for all tetracyclines, and the results can be applied to chlortetracycline, demeclocycline, doxycycline, methacycline, minocycline, and oxytetracycline. However, certain organisms may be more susceptible to doxycycline and minocycline than to tetracycline.

[i]The sulfisoxazole disk can be used for any of the commercially available sul-fonamides. Blood-containing media, except media containing lysed horse blood, are not satisfactory for testing sulfonamides. The Mueller-Hinton agar should be as thymidine-free as possible for sulfonamide and/or trimetho-prim testing.

[j]Susceptibility data for cinoxacin, nalidixic acid, nitrofurantoin, norfloxacin, sulfonamides, and trimethoprim apply only to organisms isolated from urinary tract infections.

[k]The category "intermediate" should be reported. It generally indicates that the test result be considered equivocal or indeterminate.

Chemical Agents of Control: Chemotherapeutic Agents

138

Name   Section   Date

OBSERVATIONS AND RESULTS

PART A: Kirby-Bauer Antibiotic Sensitivity Test Procedure

1. Examine all plate cultures for the presence or absence of a zone of inhibition surrounding each disc.
2. Using a ruler graduated in millimeters, carefully measure each zone of inhibition to the nearest millimeter and record your results in the chart.
3. Compare your results with Table 2 and indicate in the chart the susceptibility of each test organism to the chemotherapeutic agent as resistant (R), intermediate (I), or sensitive (S).

✚ *Refer to the color-plate insert for illustration of this reaction.*

	Gram-Negative						Acid-Fast	
	E. coli		*P. aeruginosa*		*P. vulgaris*		*M. smegmatis*	
Chemotherapeutic Agent	**Zone Size**	**Susceptibility**	**Zone Size**	**Susceptibility**	**Zone Size**	**Susceptibility**	**Zone Size**	**Susceptibility**
Penicillin								
Streptomycin								
Tetracycline								
Chloramphenicol								
Gentamicin								
Vancomycin								
Sulfanilamide								

	Gram-Positive					
	S. aureus		*E. faecalis*		*B. cereus*	
Chemotherapeutic Agent	**Zone Size**	**Susceptibility**	**Zone Size**	**Susceptibility**	**Zone Size**	**Susceptibility**
Penicillin						
Streptomycin						
Tetracycline						
Chloramphenicol						
Gentamicin						
Vancomycin						
Sulfanilamide						

4. For each of the chemotherapeutic agents, indicate:
   a. The spectrum of its activity as broad or limited.
   b. The type or types of organisms it is effective against as gram-positive, gram-negative, or acid-fast.

Chemotherapeutic Agent	Spectrum of Activity	Type(s) of Microorganisms
Penicillin		
Streptomycin		
Tetracycline		
Chloramphenicol		
Gentamicin		
Vancomycin		
Sulfanilamide		

PART B: Synergistic Effect of Drug Combinations

Examine all agar plate cultures to determine the zone of inhibition patterns exhibited. Distinctly separate zones of inhibition are indicative of an additive effect, whereas a merging of the inhibitory zones is indicative of synergism. Record your observations and results in the chart.

✚ *Refer to the color-plate insert for illustration of these reactions.*

Cultures	Appearance of Zone of Inhibition	Synergistic or Additive Effect
E. coli:		
trimethoprim and sulfisoxazole	_____	_____
trimethoprim and tetracycline	_____	_____
S. aureus:		
trimethoprim and sulfisoxazole	_____	_____
trimethoprim and tetracycline	_____	_____

REVIEW QUESTION

1. 🔍 Your experimental results indicate that antibiotics such as tetracycline, streptomycin, and chloramphenicol have a broad spectrum of activity against prokaryotic cells. Why do these antibiotics lack inhibitory activity against eukaryotic cells such as fungi?

17

Chemical Agents of Control: Disinfectants and Antiseptics

Antiseptics and disinfectants are chemical substances used to prevent contamination and infection. Many are available commercially for disinfection and asepsis.

Table 1 shows the major groups of antimicrobial agents, their modes and ranges of action, and their practical uses.

TABLE 1   Chemical Agents—Disinfectants and Antiseptics

Agent	Mechanism of Action	Use
Phenolic Compounds		
Phenol	1. Germicidal effect caused by alteration of protein structure resulting in protein denaturation. 2. Surface-active agent (surfactant) precipitates cellular proteins and disrupts cell membranes. (Phenol has been replaced by better disinfectants that are less irritating, less toxic to tissues, and better inhibitors of microorganisms.)	1. 5% solution: Disinfection. 2. 0.5% to 1% solutions: Antiseptic effect and relief of itching as it exerts a local anesthetic effect on sensory nerve endings.
Cresols	1. Similar to phenol. 2. Poisonous and must be used externally. 3. 50% solution of cresols in vegetable oil, known as Lysol®.	2% to 5% Lysol solutions used as disinfectants.
Hexachlorophene	Germicidal activity similar to phenol. (This agent is to be used with care, especially on infants, because after absorption it may cause neurotoxic effects.)	1. Reduction of pathogenic organisms on skin; added to detergents, soaps, lotions, and creams. 2. Effective against gram-positive organisms. 3. An antiseptic used topically.
Resorcinol	1. Germicidal activity similar to that of phenol. 2. Acts by precipitating cell protein.	1. Antiseptic. 2. Keratolytic agent for softening or dissolving keratin in epidermis.
Hexylresorcinol	Germicidal activity similar to that of phenol.	1. Treatment of worm infections. 2. Urinary antiseptic.

From *Microbiology: A Laboratory Manual*, Sixth Edition, James G. Cappuccino and Natalie Sherman. Copyright © 2002 Pearson Education, Inc., publishing as Benjamin Cummings. All rights reserved.

142

TABLE 1   Chemical Agents—Disinfectants and Antiseptics (continued)

Agent	Mechanism of Action	Use
Thymol	1. Related to the cresols. 2. More effective than phenol.	1. Antifungal activity. 2. Treatment of hookworm infections. 3. Mouthwashes and gargle solutions.
Alcohols Ethyl: CH_3CH_2OH Isopropyl: $(CH_3)_2CHOH$	1. Lipid solvent. 2. Denaturation and coagulation of proteins. 3. Wetting agent used in tinctures to increase the wetting ability of other chemicals. 4. Germicidal activity increases with increasing molecular weight.	Skin antiseptics: Ethyl—50% to 70%. Isopropyl—75%.
Halogens Chlorine compounds: Sodium hypochlorite (Dakin's fluid): NaOCl Chloramine: $CH_3C_6H_4SO_2NNaCl$	1. Germicidal effect resulting from rapid combination with proteins. 2. Chlorine reacts with water to form hypochlorous acid, which is bactericidal. 3. Oxidizing agent. 4. Noncompetitively inhibits enzymes, especially those dealing with glucose metabolism, by reacting with SH and NH_2 groups on the enzyme molecule.	1. Water purification. 2. Sanitation of utensils in dairy and restaurant industries. 3. Chloramine, 0.1% to 2% solutions, for wound irrigation and dressings. 4. Microbicidal.
Iodine compounds: Tincture of iodine Povidone-iodine solution (Betadine)	1. Mechanism of action is not entirely known, but it is believed that it precipitates proteins. 2. Surface-active agent.	1. Tinctures of iodine are used for skin antisepsis. 2. Treatment of goiter. 3. Effective against spores, fungi, and viruses.
Heavy Metals Mercury compounds: Inorganic: Mercury bichloride Mercurial ointments	1. Mercuric ion brings about precipitation of cellular proteins. 2. Noncompetitive inhibition of specific enzymes caused by reaction with sulfhydryl group (SH) on enzymes of bacterial cells.	1. Inorganic mercurials are irritating to tissues, toxic systemically, adversely affected by organic matter, and have no action on spores. 2. Mercury compounds are mainly used as disinfectants of laboratory materials.
Organic mercurials: Mercurochrome (merbromin) Merthiolate (thimerosal) Metaphen (nitromersol) Merbak (acetomeroctol)	1. Similar to those of inorganic mercurials, but in proper concentrations are useful antiseptics. 2. Much less irritating than inorganic mercurials.	1. Less toxic, less irritating; used mainly for skin asepsis. 2. Do not kill spores.
Silver compounds: Silver nitrate	1. Precipitate cellular proteins. 2. Interfere with metabolic activities of microbial cells. 3. Inorganic salts are germicidal.	Asepsis of mucous membrane of throat and eyes.

Chemical Agents of Control: Disinfectants and Antiseptics

143

TABLE 1 Chemical Agents—Disinfectants and Antiseptics (continued)

Agent	Mechanism of Action	Use
Surface-Active Agents Wetting agents: Emulsifiers, soaps, and detergents	1. Lower surface tension and aid in mechanical removal of bacteria and soil. 2. If active portion of the agent carries a negative electric charge, it is called an anionic surface-active agent. If active portion of the agent carries a positive electric charge, it is called a cationic surface-active agent. 3. Exert bactericidal activity by interfering with or by depressing metabolic activities of microorganisms. 4. Disrupt cell membranes. 5. Alter cell permeability.	Weak action against fungi, acid-fast microorganisms, spores, and viruses.

Cationic agents:
  Quaternary ammonium compounds
  Benzalkonium chloride
	1. Lower surface tension because of keratolytic, detergent, and emulsifying properties.
	
	2. Their germicidal activities are reduced by soaps.
		1. Bactericidal, fungicidal; inactive against spores and viruses.
		
		2. Asepsis of intact skin.
		
		3. Disinfectant for operating-room equipment.
		
		4. Dairy and restaurant sanitization.

^nionic agents:
  Tincture of green soap
  Sodium tetradecyl sulfate
	1. Neutral or alkaline salts of high-molecular-weight acids. Common soaps included in this group.
	
	2. Exert their maximum activity in an acid medium and are most effective against gram-positive cells.
	
	3. Same as all surface-active agents.
		1. Cleansing agent.
		
		2. Sclerosing agent in treatment of varicose veins and internal hemorrhoids.

Acids (H^+) **Alkali** (OH^-)	1. Destruction of cell wall and cell membrane. 2. Coagulation of proteins.	Disinfection; however, of little practical value.
Formaldehyde (liquid or gas)	Alkylating agent causes reduction of enzymes.	1. Room disinfection. 2. Alcoholic solution for instrument disinfection. 3. Specimen preservation.
Ethylene Oxide	Alkylating agent causes reduction of enzymes.	Sterilization of heat-labile material.
β-Propiolactone (liquid or gas)	Alkylating agent causes reduction of enzymes.	1. Sterilization of tissue for grafting. 2. Destruction of hepatitis virus. 3. Room disinfection.
Basic Dyes Crystal violet	Affinity for nucleic acids; interfere with reproduction in gram-positive organisms.	1. Skin antiseptic. 2. Laboratory isolation of gram-negative bacteria.

Chemical Agents of Control: Disinfectants and Antiseptics

The efficiency of all disinfectants and antiseptics is influenced by a variety of factors, including the following:

1. **Concentration:** The concentration of a chemical substance markedly influences its effect on microorganisms, with higher concentrations producing a more rapid death. Concentration cannot be arbitrarily determined; the toxicity of the chemical to the tissues being treated and the damaging effect on nonliving materials must also be considered.

2. **Length of exposure:** All microbes are not destroyed within the same exposure time. Sensitive forms are destroyed more rapidly than resistant ones. The longer the exposure to the agent, the greater its antimicrobial activity. The toxicity of the chemical and environmental conditions must be considered in assessing the length of time necessary for disinfection or asepsis.

3. **Type of microbial population to be destroyed:** Microorganisms vary in their susceptibility to destruction by chemicals. Bacterial spores are the most resistant for--- Capsulated bacteria are more re   t than noncapsulated forms; acid-fast bacteria are more resistant than non–acid-fast; and older, metabolically less active cells are more resistant than younger cells. Awareness of the types of microorganisms that may be present will influence the choice of agent.

4. **Environmental conditions:** Conditions under which a disinfectant or antiseptic affects the chemical agent are as follows:

   a. **Temperature:** Cells are killed as the result of a chemical reaction between the agent and cellular component. As increasing temperatures increase the rate of chemical reactions, application of heat during disinfection markedly increases the rate at which the microbial population is destroyed.

   b. **pH:** The pH conditions during disinfection may affect not only the microorganisms but also the compound. Extremes in pH are harmful to many microorganisms and may enhance the antimicrobial action of a chemical. Deviation from a neutral pH may cause ionization of the disinfectant;

depending on the chemical agent, this may serve to increase or decrease the chemical's microbicidal action.

   c. **Type of material on which the microorganisms exist:** The destructive power of the compound on cells is due to its combination with organic cellular molecules. If the material on which the microorganisms are found is primarily organic, such as blood, pus, or tissue fluids, the agent will combine with these extracellular organic molecules, and its antimicrobial activity will be reduced.

Numerous laboratory procedures are available for evaluating the antimicrobial efficiency of disinfectants or antiseptics. They provide a general rather than an absolute measure of the effectiveness of any agent because test conditions frequently differ considerably from those seen during practical use. Two commonly employed procedures are presented.

PART A: Phenol Coefficient

PURPOSE

To compare the effectiveness of disinfectants.

PRINCIPLE

The **phenol coefficient test** compares the antimicrobial activity of a chemical compound to that of phenol under standardized experimental conditions. Equal quantities of a series of dilutions of the chemical being tested and of pure phenol are placed into sterile test tubes. A standardized quantity of a pure culture of the test microorganisms, such as *Staphylococcus aureus* or *Salmonella typhi*, is added to each of the tubes. Subcultures of the test microorganism are made from each dilution of the test chemicals into sterile broth media at intervals of 5, 10, and 15 minutes after introduction of the organisms. All the subcultures are incubated at 37°C for 48 hours and examined for the presence or absence of growth.

The phenol coefficient is determined by dividing the highest dilution of the chemical being tested that destroyed the microorganisms in 10 minutes but not in 5 minutes by

TABLE 2 Illustration of Phenol Coefficient Determination

Chemical Agent and Dilution		Presence of Growth in Subcultures (minutes)		
		5	10	15
Phenol	1:80	−	−	−
	1:90	+	−	−
	1:100	+	+	−
Test chemical	1:400	−	−	−
	1:450	+	−	−
	1:500	+	+	−

Test chemical dilution of 1:450 showed growth at 5 minutes but no growth at 10 minutes.
Phenol dilution of 1:90 showed growth at 5 minutes but no growth at 10 minutes.
Phenol coefficient of test chemical = 450/90 = 5.

the highest dilution of phenol that destroyed the microorganism in 10 minutes but not in 5 minutes. A phenol coefficient no greater than 1 indicates that this agent is as effective as or less effective than phenol. A phenol coefficient greater than 1 suggests that the chemical is more effective than phenol when employed under test conditions. A phenol coefficient of 5 indicates that the chemical agent under evaluation is five times as effective as phenol. Table 2 illustrates a phenol coefficient determination.

MATERIALS

Cultures

24-hour nutrient broth cultures of *Staphylococcus aureus* dispensed in sterile dropper-bottles.

Media

Per designated student group: 19 nutrient broth tubes.

Disinfectants

Per designated student group: phenol dilutions: 1:80, 1:90, 1:100; Lysol dilutions: 1:400, 1:450, 1:500.

Equipment

Bunsen burner, inoculating loop, test-tube rack, and glassware marking pencil.

PROCEDURE

1. Label 18 nutrient broth tubes with the name and dilution of the disinfectant and the time interval of subculturing (e.g., phenol 1:80, 5 minutes).

2. In a test-tube rack, place one test tube of each of the different phenol and Lysol dilutions.

3. Rapidly introduce one drop of the *S. aureus* culture into each of the test tubes of disinfectant. Note the time when you start introducing the microorganisms into the disinfectants.

4. Agitate all the test tubes to ensure contact between the disinfectant and the microbes.

5. Using sterile technique, at intervals of 5, 10, and 15 minutes transfer one loopful from each of the test tubes containing the disinfectant and microorganisms into the appropriately labeled sterile tube of nutrient broth.

6. Incubate all nutrient broth cultures for 48 hours at 37°C.

PART B: Agar Plate–Sensitivity Method

PURPOSE

To evaluate the effectiveness of antiseptic agents against selected test organisms.

Chemical Agents of Control: Disinfectants and Antiseptics

PRINCIPLE

This procedure requires the heavy inoculation of an agar plate with the test organism. Sterile, color-coded filter-paper discs are impregnated with a different antiseptic and equally spaced on the inoculated agar plate. Following incubation, the agar plate is examined for zones of inhibition (areas of no microbial growth) surrounding the discs. A zone of inhibition is indicative of microbicidal activity against the organism. Absence of a zone of inhibition indicates that the chemical was ineffective against the test organism. **Note:** The size of the zone of inhibition is not indicative of the degree of effectiveness of the chemical agent.

MATERIALS

Cultures

24- to 48-hour trypticase soy broth cultures of *Escherichia coli*, *Bacillus cereus*, *Staphylococcus aureus*, and *Mycobacterium smegmatis*.

Media

Per designated student group: four trypticase soy agar plates.

Antiseptics/Disinfectants

Per designated student group: 10 ml of each of the following dispensed in 25-ml beakers: tincture of iodine, 3% hydrogen peroxide, 70% isopropyl alcohol, and 5% chlorine bleach.

Equipment

Four different-colored, sterile Sensi-discs™, forceps, sterile cotton swabs, Bunsen burner, and glassware marking pencil.

PROCEDURE

1. Aseptically inoculate the appropriately labeled agar plates with their respective test organisms by streaking each plate in horizontal and vertical directions and around the edge with a sterile swab.

2. Color-code the Sensi-discs according to the chemical agents to be used (e.g., red = chlorine bleach).

3. Using forceps dipped in alcohol and flamed, expose four discs of the same color by placing them into the solution of one of the chemical agents. Drain the saturated discs on absorbent paper immediately prior to placing one on each of the inoculated agar plates. Place each disc approximately 2 cm in from the edge of the plate. Gently press the discs down with the forceps so that they adhere to the surface of the agar.

4. Impregnate the remaining discs as described in Step 3. Place one of each of the three remaining colored discs on the surface of each of the four inoculated agar plates equidistant from each other around the periphery of the plate.

5. Incubate all plate cultures in an inverted position for 24 to 48 hours at 37°C.

Name   Section   Date

OBSERVATIONS AND RESULTS

PART A: Phenol Coefficient

1. Observe all nutrient broth cultures for the presence of growth. Use the sterile test tube of nutrient broth as a control in determining the presence or absence of growth.
2. Record your observations in the chart as growth (+) or no growth (−).

Disinfectant	Dilution	Growth in Subcultures (minutes)		
		5	10	15
Phenol	1:80			
	1:90			
	1:100			
Lysol	1:400			
	1:450			
	1:500			

3. Calculate the phenol coefficient of Lysol.

PART B: Agar Plate–Sensitivity Method

1. Observe all the plates for the presence of a zone of inhibition surrounding each of the impregnated discs.
2. Record your observations in the chart as absence of a zone of inhibition (0), or presence of a zone of inhibition (+).

✚ *Refer to the color-plate insert for illustration of the reaction.*

Bacterial Species	Antimicrobial Agent			
	Tincture of Iodine	3% Hydrogen Peroxide	70% Isopropyl Alcohol	5% Chlorine Bleach
E. coli gram-negative				
S. aureus gram-positive				
M. smegmatis acid-fast				
B. cereus spore-former				

Chemical Agents of Control: Disinfectants and Antiseptics

3. Indicate which of the antiseptics exhibited microbicidal activity against each of the following groups of microorganisms.

Bacterial Group	Tincture of Iodine	3% Hydrogen Peroxide	70% Isopropyl Alcohol	5% Chlorine Bleach
Gram-negative				
Gram-positive				
Acid-fast				
Spore-former				

4. Which of the experimental chemical compounds appears to have the broadest range of microbicidal activity? The narrowest range of microbicidal activity?

REVIEW QUESTIONS

1. Evaluate the effectiveness of a disinfectant with a phenol coefficient of 40.

2. Can the disinfection period (exposure time) be arbitrarily increased? Explain.

3. A household cleanser is labeled germicidal. Explain what this means to you.

Physical Methods of Control: Heat

The successful man lengthens his stride when he discovers that the sign post has deceived him; the failure looks for a place to sit down.

JOHN R. ROGERS

Objectives

After completing this exercise, you should be able to:

1. Compare the bactericidal effectiveness of dry heat and moist heat on different species of bacteria.
2. Evaluate the heat tolerance of microbes.
3. Define and provide a use for each of the following: incineration, hot air oven, pasteurization, boiling, and autoclaving.

Background

The use of extreme temperature to control the growth of microbes is widely employed. Generally, if heat is applied, bacteria are killed; if cold temperatures are used, bacterial growth is inhibited.

Bacteria exhibit different tolerances to the application of heat. Heat sensitivity is genetically determined and is partially reflected in the optimal growth ranges (Exercise 20), which are **psychrophilic** (0°C to 20°C), **mesophilic** (25°C to 40°C), and **thermophilic** (45°C to 65°C), and by the presence of heat-resistant endospores. Overall, bacteria are more heat resistant than most other forms of life. Heat sensitivity of organisms can be affected by container size, cell density, moisture content, pH, and medium composition.

Heat can be applied as dry or moist heat. **Dry heat,** such as that in hot air ovens or incineration (for example, flaming loops), denatures enzymes, dehydrates microbes, and kills by oxidation effects. A standard application of dry heat in a hot air oven is 170°C for 2 hours. The heat of hot air is not readily transferred to a cooler body such as a microbial cell. Moisture transfers heat energy to the microbial cell more efficiently than dry air, resulting in the denaturation of enzymes. **Moist heat** methods include pasteurization, boiling, and autoclaving. In **pasteurization** the temperature is maintained at 63°C for 30 minutes or 72°C for 15 seconds to kill designated organisms that are pathogenic or cause spoilage. **Boiling** (100°C) for 10 minutes will kill vegetative bacterial cells; however, endospores are

Table 1

Relationship Between Pressure and Temperature of Steam

Pressure (pounds per square inch, psi, in excess of atmospheric pressure)	Temperature (°C)
0 psi	100°C
5 psi	110°C
10 psi	116°C
15 psi	121°C
20 psi	126°C
30 psi	135°C

Source: G. J. Tortora, B. R. Funke, and C. L. Case. *Microbiology: An Introduction,* 7th ed. San Francisco, CA: Benjamin Cummings, 2001.

not inactivated. The most effective method of moist heat sterilization is **autoclaving,** the use of steam under pressure. Increased pressure raises the boiling point of water and produces steam with a higher temperature (Table 1). Standard conditions for autoclaving are 15 psi, 121°C for 15 minutes. This is usually sufficient to kill endospores and render materials sterile.

There are two different methods of measuring heat effectiveness. **Thermal death time (TDT)** is the length of time required to kill all bacteria in a liquid culture at a given temperature. The less common **thermal death point (TDP)** is the temperature required to kill all bacteria in a liquid culture in 10 minutes.

Materials

Petri plates containing nutrient agar (2)

Thermometer

Empty tube

Beaker

Hot plate or tripod and asbestos pad

Ice

Cultures (as assigned)

Group A:
    Old (48 to 72 hours) *Bacillus subtilis*
    Young (24 hours) *Bacillus subtilis*

Group B:
    Staphylococcus epidermidis
    Escherichia coli

Group C:
    Young (24 hours) *Bacillus subtilis*
    Escherichia coli

Group D:
    Mold (*Penicillium*) spore suspension
    Old (48 to 72 hours) *Bacillus subtilis*

Demonstration

Autoclaved and dry-heated soil

Techniques Required

Inoculating loop

Aseptic technique

Plate streaking

Procedure

Each pair of students is assigned two cultures and a temperature.

Group	Group
A: 63°C _____	A: 72°C _____
B: 63°C _____	B: 72°C _____
C: 63°C _____	C: 72°C _____
D: 63°C _____	D: 72°C _____

You can share beakers of water as long as the effect of the same temperature is being evaluated.

1. Divide two plates of nutrient agar into five sections each. Label the sections "0," "15 sec," "2 min," "5 min," and "15 min."
2. Set up a water bath in the beaker, with the water level higher than the level of the broth in the tubes. Do not put the broth tubes into the water bath at this time. Carefully put the thermometer in a test tube of water in the bath.
3. Streak the assigned organisms on the "0" time section of the appropriate plate. Why are we using "old" and "young" *Bacillus* cultures? _____ _____
4. Raise the temperature of the bath to the desired temperature and maintain that temperature. Use ice to adjust the temperature. Why was 63°C selected as one of the temperatures? _____ _____
5. Place the broth tubes of your organism into the bath when the temperature is at the desired point. After 15 seconds, remove the tubes, resuspend the culture, streak a loopful on the corresponding sections, and return the tubes to the water bath. Repeat at 2, 5, and 15 minutes. What is the longest time period that any microbe is exposed to heat? _____
6. When you are done, clean the beaker and return the materials. Incubate the plates, inverted, at 35°C until the next lab period. Record your results and the results for the other organisms tested: (–) = no growth; (+) = minimum growth; (2+) = moderate growth; (3+) = heavy growth; and (4+) = maximum growth.
7. Examine the demonstration plates, and record your observations. (Refer to color plate V.6.) Collect results from your classmates to complete the data table in your Laboratory Report.

Physical Methods of Control: Heat

LABORATORY REPORT

Name _____

Date _____

Lab Section _____

Purpose _____

_____

_____

Data

Record growth on a scale from (–) to (4+).

Organism	Temperature/Time									
	63°C					72°C				
	0	15 sec	2 min	5 min	15 min	0	15 sec	2 min	5 min	15 min
Old *Bacillus subtilis*										
Young *Bacillus subtilis*										
Staphylococcus epidermidis										
Escherichia coli										
Mold (*Penicillium*) spores										

Demonstration Plates

	Control	Autoclaved	Dry-Heated
Number of colonies			
Number of different colonies			

Graph your cultures at 63°C.   at 72°C.

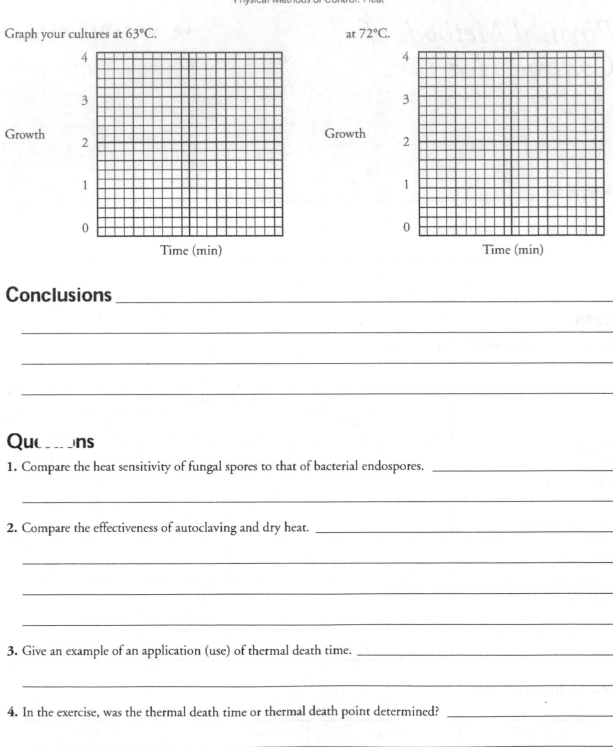

Conclusions _____

_____

_____

_____

Questions

1. Compare the heat sensitivity of fungal spores to that of bacterial endospores. _____

_____

2. Compare the effectiveness of autoclaving and dry heat. _____

_____

_____

_____

3. Give an example of an application (use) of thermal death time. _____

_____

4. In the exercise, was the thermal death time or thermal death point determined? _____

_____

5. Give an example of a nonlaboratory use of each of the following methods to control microbial growth:

    a. Incineration: _____

    b. Pasteurization: _____

    c. Autoclaving: _____

6. Define pasteurization. What is the purpose of pasteurization? _____

_____

_____

_____

Critical Thinking

1. Explain why fungi and *Bacillus* sometimes grow better after heat treatment.

2. The decimal reduction time (DRT value) is the time it takes to kill 90% of cells present. Assume that a DRT value for autoclaving a culture is 1.5 minutes. How long would it take to kill all the cells if 10^6 cells were present? What would happen if you stopped the heating process after 9 minutes?

3. Indicators are used in autoclaving to ensure that sterilization is complete. One type of chemical indicator turns color when it has reached a specific temperature; the other type turns color when it has reached a specified temperature and been exposed to steam. Which type of indicator should be used?

4. A biological indicator used in autoclaving is a vial containing 10^9 *Bacillus stearothermophilus* cells that is placed in the autoclave with the material to be sterilized. After autoclaving, the vial is incubated and examined for growth. Why is this species used as opposed to *E. coli* or *B. subtilis*?

Physical Methods of Control: Ultraviolet Radiation

Objectives

After completing this exercise, you should be able to:

1. Examine the effects of ultraviolet radiation on bacteria.
2. Explain the method of action of ultraviolet radiation and light repair of mutations.

Background

Radiant energy comes to the Earth from the Sun and other extraterrestrial sources, and some is generated on Earth from natural and human-made sources. The **radiant energy spectrum** is shown in Figure 1. Radiation differs in wavelength and energy. The shorter .elengths have more energy. X rays and gamma rays ... forms of **ionizing radiation.** Their principal effect is to ionize water into *highly reactive free radicals* (with unpaired electrons) that can break strands of DNA. The effect of radiation is influenced by many variables, such as the age of the cells, media composition, and temperature.

Some **nonionizing** wavelengths are essential for biochemical processes. The main absorption wavelengths for green algae, green plants, and photosynthetic bacteria are shown in Figure 1a. Animal cells synthesize vitamin D in the presence of light around 300 nm. Nonionizing radiation between 15 and 390 nm is called **ultraviolet (UV).** Wavelengths below 200 nm are absorbed by air and do not reach living organisms. The most lethal wavelengths, sometimes called biocidal, are in the **UVC** range, 200–290 nm. These wavelengths correspond to the optimal absorption wavelengths of DNA (Figure 1b). **UVB** wavelengths (290–320 nm) can also cause damage to DNA. **UVA** wavelengths (320–400 nm) are not as readily absorbed and are therefore less active on living organisms.

Ultraviolet light induces *pyrimidine dimers* in the nucleic acid, which result in a mutation. Mutations in critical genes result in the death of the cell unless the damage is repaired. When pyrimidine dimers are exposed to visible light, photolyases are activated; these enzymes split the dimers. This is called **light repair** or **photoreactivation.** Another repair mechanism, called **dark repair,** is independent of light. Dimers are removed by endonuclease, DNA polymerase replaces the bases, and DNA ligase seals the sugar-phosphate backbone.

As a sterilizing agent, ultraviolet radiation is limited by its poor penetrating ability. It is used to sterilize some heat-labile solutions, to decontaminate hospital operating rooms and food-processing areas, and to disinfect wastewater.

In this exercise, we will investigate the effects of ultraviolet radiation and light repair using lamps of the desired wavelength.

Materials

Petri plates containing nutrient agar (3)

Sterile cotton swabs (3)

Covers (choose one): Gauze; 3, 6, or 12 layers of paper; cloth; aluminum foil; clear glass; sunglasses; or plastic

Ultraviolet lamp (265 nm)

Cultures (one of the following)

Serratia marcescens

Bacillus subtilis

Saccharomyces cerevisiae

Techniques Required

Inoculating loop

Aseptic technique

Procedure

1. Swab the surface of each plate with *one* of the cultures; to ensure complete coverage, swab the surface in two directions. Label the plates "A," "B," and "C."
2. Remove the lid of an inoculated plate and cover one-half of the plate with one of the covering materials (Figure 2). Cover one-half of each of r' remaining plates with the same material.

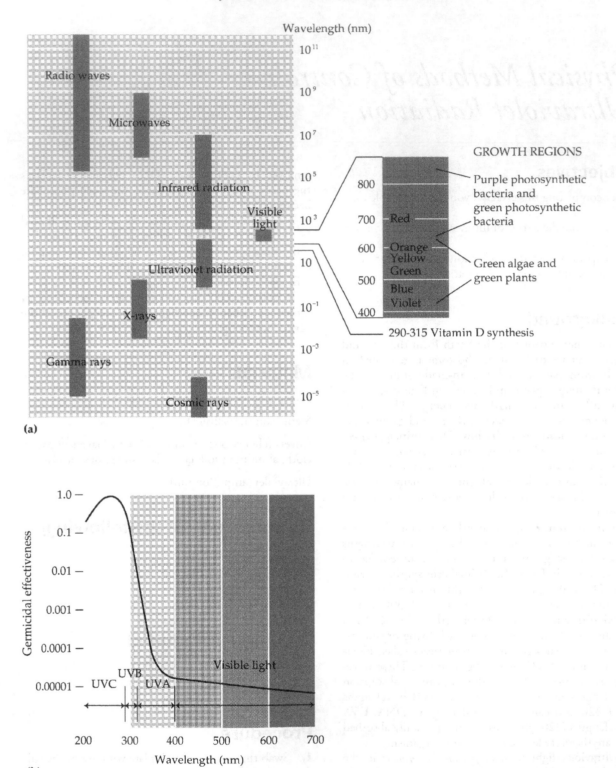

(a)

(b)

Figure 1

Radiant energy. (a) Radiant energy spectrum and absorption of light for photosynthesis. (b) Biocidal effectiveness of radiant energy between 200 and 700 nanometers (nm) (from UV to visible red light).

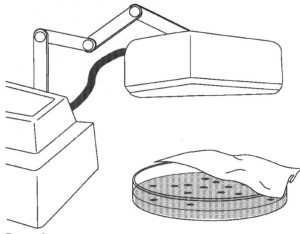

Figure 2

With the lid removed, cover one-half of an inoculated Petri plate with one of the covering materials.

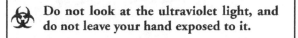

Do not look at the ultraviolet light, and do not leave your hand exposed to it.

3. Place each plate directly under the ultraviolet light 24 cm from the light with the *cover off*, agar-side up. Why should the cover be removed? _____

_____

Plate A: Expose for 30 seconds. Replace the lid and incubate (22°C).

Plate B: Expose for 30 seconds and incubate in sunlight. Replace the Petri plate lid and cover the plate with a piece of glass.

Plate C: Expose for 15 seconds. Replace the lid and incubate in a dark incubator (22°C).

4. Incubate all three plates, inverted, at 22°C or at room temperature until the next period.

5. Examine all plates and record your results. Observe the results of students using the other organisms.

158

Physical Methods of Control: Ultraviolet Radiation

Name _____

Date _____

Lab Section _____

Purpose _____

_____

_____

Data

What organism did you use? _____

What did you use to cover one-half of each plate? _____

Sketch your results. Note any pigmentation.

A   B   C

Classmates' results from other organisms: _____

_____

_____

Conclusions _____

_____

_____

Questions

1. If the *Bacillus* had sporulated before exposure to radiation, would that affect the results? _____

_____

_____

2. What are the variables in ultraviolet radiation treatment? ___ _____

_____

3. Many of the microorganisms found on environmental surfaces are pigmented. Of what possible advantage is the

pigment? ___ _____

_____

_____

Critical Thinking

1. Can dark repair be a factor in this experiment?

2. Why are there still some colonies growing in the areas exposed to ultraviolet light?

3. How might the results differ if a UVA lamp were used? A UVB lamp?

4. Considering your results, discuss the possible effects of UV radiation on the ecology of a lake if the UV radiation has the same effect on the lake bacteria as it did on the bacteria in your experiment.

Other Influences on Microbial Growth: Osmotic Pressure and pH

Objectives

After completing this exercise, you should be able to:

1. Define osmotic pressure and explain how it affects a cell.
2. Explain how microbial growth is related to osmotic pressure and pH.
3. Prepare and use a gradient plate.

Background

The osmotic pressure of an environment influences microbial growth. **Osmotic pressure** is the force with which a solvent (water) moves from a solution of lower solute concentration to a solution of higher solute concentration across a semipermeable membrane (Figure
The addition of solutes, especially salts and sugars,
the resultant increase in osmotic pressure, are used to preserve some foods. Can you name a food that is preserved with salt? _____
With sugar? _____

Bacteria are often able to live in a **hypotonic** (hypoosmotic) environment, in which the concentration of solutes outside the cell is lower than that inside the cell. However, when the concentration of solutes outside the cell is higher than that inside the cell—a **hypertonic** (hyperosmotic) environment—a bacterial cell will undergo plasmolysis. *Plasmolysis* occurs when water leaves the cell and the cytoplasmic membrane draws inward, away from the cell wall. A few bacteria, called **facultative halophiles,** are able to tolerate salt concentrations up to 10%, and **extreme halophiles** require 15% to 20% salt.

The acidity or alkalinity (**pH**) of the environment also influences microbial growth. Optimal bacterial growth usually occurs between pH 6.5 and pH 7.5. Only a few bacteria grow at an acidic pH below 4.0. Therefore, organic acids are used to preserve foods such as fermented dairy products.

Many bacteria produce acids that may inhibit their growth. **Buffers** are added to culture media to neutralize these acids. The peptones in complex media act as buffers. Phosphate salts are often used as buffers in chemically defined media.

In this exercise, we will compare bacterial growth to fungal growth. Fungi differ from bacteria morphologically and biochemically. The yeast and mold used here are microbes belonging to the Kingdom Fungi.

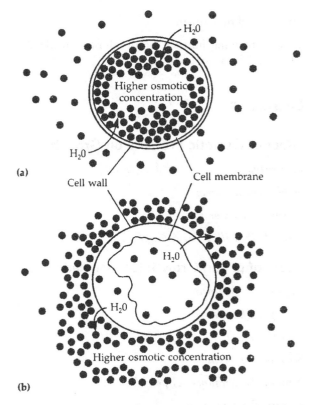

(a)
Cell wall   Cell membrane

(b)

Figure 1
Osmotic pressure. **(a)** Water moves into the cell in a hypotonic solution. **(b)** Water leaves the cell in a hypertonic environment.

Materials

Effect of Osmotic Pressure on Growth

(Your instructor will assign salt, sugar, or nutrient agar control.)

Petri plates containing nutrient agar + 5%, 10%, 15% NaCl (one of each) *or*

Petri plates containing nutrient agar + 10%, 25%, 50% sucrose (one of each) *or*

Petri plate containing nutrient agar

Gradient Plate

Sterile Petri dish

Tube containing melted nutrient agar

Tube containing melted nutrient agar + 25% NaCl *or* 50% sucrose

Salt *or* sugar enrichments

Effect of pH on Growth

Tubes containing nutrient broth adjusted to pH 2.5, 5.0, 7.0, 9.5 (one of each)

Cultures

Effect of Osmotic Pressure on Growth

Escherichia coli

Staphylococcus aureus

A yeast (*Saccharomyces*)

A mold (*Penicillium* or *Aspergillus*)

Effect of pH on Growth (as assigned)

Staphy   s aureus

Alcaligenes faecalis

Escherichia coli

Serratia marcescens

A mold (*Penicillium* or *Aspergillus*)

A yeast (*Saccharomyces*)

Techniques Required

Inoculating loop

Plate streaking

Procedure

Effect of Osmotic Pressure on Growth

1. Obtain a set of nutrient agar + salt *or* nutrient agar + sucrose plates. Draw two crossed lines to form four quadrants on the bottom of one plate. Each quadrant will be inoculated with one of the organisms and should be labeled accordingly (Figure 2). Repeat this procedure until all plates are marked. One student group will mark the *control* plate (nutrient agar alone). What is the purpose of the control plate? _____

_____

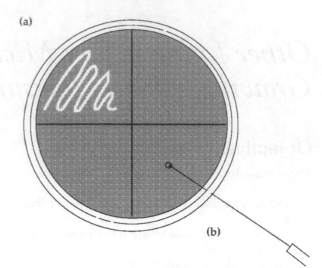

(a)

(b)

Figure 2

Inoculate each plate with four organisms. (**a**) Streak bacteria and yeast cultures. (**b**) Place a loopful of mold suspension in the center of one quadrant.

2. Using a sterile loop, inoculate *S. aureus* onto one quadrant on each plate (Figure 2a). Repeat this procedure to inoculate *E. coli* and the yeast.
3. Place a loopful of the mold suspension in the center of the remaining quadrant on each plate (Figure 2b).
4. Invert the plates and incubate them at 35°C for 24 to 48 hours. Record the relative amounts of bacterial or yeast growth; the culture showing the "best" growth is given (4+) and others are evaluated relative to that culture.
5. Incubate the plates at room temperature for 2 to 4 days, and record relative amounts of mold growth.

Gradient Plate

1. Pour a layer of nutrient agar into a sterile Petri dish and let it solidify with the dish resting on a small pencil or a loop handle (Figure 3a) so that a wedge forms.
2. On the bottom of the dish, draw a line at the end corresponding to the high side of the agar and label it "low." Draw four lines perpendicular to the first line, and if assigned sucrose, label the lines "0.5," "5," "10," and "15"; if assigned salt, "0.5," "5," "15," and "30" (Figure 3b).
3. Pour a layer of salt *or* sugar agar over the nutrient agar wedge. Let it solidify. A solute gradient concentration has been prepared. Why was the high side of the agar labeled "low" in step 2? _____

_____

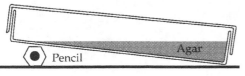

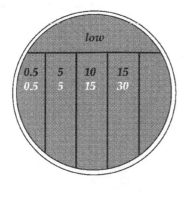

(a) Allow the nutrient agar to solidify into a wedge.

Figure 3
Gradient plate.

4. The following enrichments have been prepared:
    a. Raisins were placed in tubes of nutrient broth + 0.5% sucrose, 5% sucrose, 10% sucrose, and 15% sucrose. The enrichments were incubated for 1 week.
    b. Hamburger was inoculated into tubes of nutrient broth + 0.5% NaCl, 5% NaCl, 15% NaCl, and 30% NaCl. The enrichments were incubated for 1 week.
5. Using the enrichment with the same solute as your gradient plate, streak a loopful of each enrichment onto the agar over the prelabeled lines. Streak from the low to the high end.
6. Incubate the plate, inverted, at 35°C for 48 hours, and record the growth patterns.

Effect of pH on Growth

1. Inoculate a loopful of your organism into each tube of pH test broth.
2. Incubate the tubes at 35°C for 24 to 48 hours. Record your results and results for the organisms tested by other students.

Other Influences on Microbial Growth: Osmotic Pressure and pH

Name _____

Date _____

Lab Section _____

Purpose _____

_____

_____

Data

Effect of Osmotic Pressure on Growth

Rate the relative amounts of growth on nutrient agar and nutrient agar containing solutes (salt and sucrose): (–) = no growth; (+) = minimal growth; (2+) = moderate growth; (3+) = heavy growth; (4+) = very heavy (maximum) growth.

Medium	Organism/Amount of Growth			
	S. aureus	E. coli	Yeast	Mold
Nutrient agar				
+ 5% NaCl				
+ 10% NaCl				
+ 15% NaCl				
+ 10% sucrose				
+ 25% sucrose				
+ 50% sucrose				

Gradient Plate

Sketch your growth patterns and those of another group.

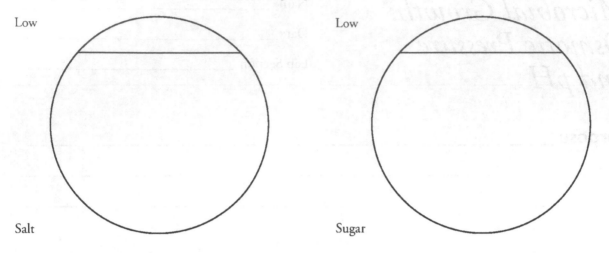

Low   Low

Salt   Sugar

Effect of pH on Growth

Record the growth (+) or lack of growth (–) of each organism used.

pH				Growth of		
	S. aureus	A. faecalis	E. coli	S. marcescens	Mold	Yeast
2.5						
5.0						
7.0						
9.5						

Conclusions

1. Which organism tolerates high concentrations of salt best? _____

   Of what advantage is this to the organism? _____

   _____

2. Which organism tolerates high concentrations of sucrose best? _____

   Why is this advantageous to the organism? _____

   _____

3. Write a statement comparing the osmotic pressure tolerance of bacteria to that of fungi. _____

_____

4. What is the pH tolerance of bacteria compared to that of fungi? _____

_____

Questions

1. Explain the growth patterns on the gradient plates. _____

_____

_____

_____

_____

2. What is the principle of the gradient plate? _____

3. What is the purpose of the nutrient agar control plate? _____

_____

4. Should (4+) growth occur only on the control plate? _____

Briefly explain. _____

_____

5. Why were the media containing raisins and hamburger labeled "enrichments"? _____

_____

6. Why are bacteria more likely to survive in a hypotonic environment than in a hypertonic environment? _____

_____

7. What is meant by "neutral pH"? _____

_____

8. Did any organisms grow in acidic conditions? _____ Why would you expect some

organisms to grow in an acidic environment? _____

_____

_____

_____

Critical Thinking

1. You are growing a bacterial culture in order to harvest a particular enzyme that the bacteria make. However, the bacteria make enough lactic acid within a few hours to kill themselves. What can you do to keep the cells growing?

2. *Helicobacter pylori* grows in the human stomach. The bacterium produces large quantities of urease. Of what value is this enzyme to the bacterium? What disease does *Helicobacter* cause?

3. The graph shows the pH (dashed line) and absorbance (solid line) of a bacterial culture over a 24-hour period. The culture medium consists of glucose and peptone. Explain the change in pH.

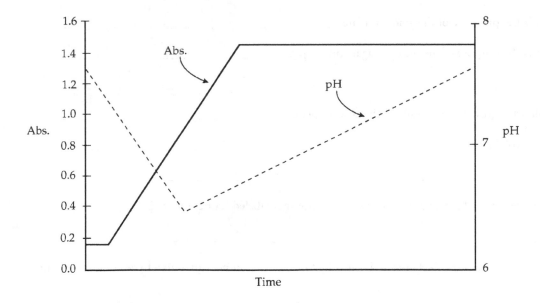

21

QUANTITATION & PRINCIPLES OF CYTOMETRY
(Direct Microscopic Cell-Count)

OBJECTIVES

1. Count microbial cells directly under the microscope using a **hemacytometer**.
2. Learn how to use a sample to determine cell density of a liquid specimen.
3. Estimate number of cells present in liquid sample.
4. Perform dilutions of dense culture for easier counting.
5. Calculate dilution factor.

PRINCIPLE

Concentration of microbial cells in a culture can be estimated indirectly by degree of cloudiness. In order to determine the number of cells suspended in a volume of liquid - like milk, drinks, broth, blood, or clinical samples – direct counting is done under the microscope using a calibrated counting chamber. The slide invented specifically for this purpose is called a **hemacytometer**.

Hemacytometer: The hemacytometer (sometimes spelled 'hemocytometer') is a glass slide with raised sides that form a counting chamber. A grid that covers an area of 9.0 mm^2 is etched into the chamber floor on both sides of the slide to form nine large squares ("W" in Figure 1a). Each large square is 1mm long, 1mm wide, and 100 m high (this also represents the chamber depth below the cover glass). This known volume makes it possible to calculate the cell concentration of a liquid sample in the counting chamber and estimate the result to the whole specimen. Counting occurs in the central square, which is subdivided into 25 squares bordered by double or triple-lines. Each square is sub-divided into 16 mini-squares (Figure 2).

MATERIALS

1. Hemacytometers
2. Cover slips
3. Compound light microscopes
4. 200 *ml* Yeast culture (lyophilized packet reconstituted in sucrose solution)
5. Plastic pipettes
6. (a) 10 *ml* graduated measuring cylinders
   (b) 100 *ml* graduated measuring cylinders
7. Dry 250*ml* Erlenmeyer flask

PROCEDURE

1. Clean hemacytometer with tap water and dry the mirror-like polished surface of the counting chamber with lens paper.
2. Using the scanning objective lens (4X), begin by locating the grid of squares etched into the chamber floor (Figure 2).
3. Select the low power (10X) objective lens and center the grid to frame the central square of 25 triple-lined squares (some brands are double-line), each subdivided into 16 mini-squares, which hold a liquid volume of 0. 00025 *mm*^{3} each (Figure 1b).

Preparing the sample:

How to Dilute Cloudy Specimens and Calculate 'Dilution Factor':

    a. Fill the 10-*ml* measuring cylinder with 9 *ml* of water and the 100-*ml* cylinder with 90 *ml* of water.

    b. Using a plastic pipette, add drops of yeast suspension to the 9 *ml* water to a final volume of 10 *ml*. Mix well using a pipette (remember: yeasts cells settle rather rapidly!)

    c. Add the diluted sample to the 90 ml water in the 100 ml cylinder.

    d. Transfer sample from 100 *ml* cylinder to 250*ml* Erlenmeyer flask for better mixing

    e. Complete Table 1, using information from Steps **b & c** above:

Table 1: Determination of Dilution Factor

Dilution Step	Specimen Volume ('A' *ml*)	Volume of Water ('B' *ml*)	Final Volume ('C' *ml*)	Original Sample in Final Volume (A : C)	Dilution Factor (C)
STEP B					
STEP C					

4. Place a cover glass on the raised edges around the counting surface.

5. **How to Load the slide**: Swirl the flask to re-suspend the yeast cells and mix the diluted sample. Use the plastic pipette to take some sample and introduce it under the cover glass through the V-shaped groove on the side of the slide. The sample will be drawn into the counting chamber by capillary action to just cover the reflective surface.

6. Use the fine adjustment to bring both the counting grid and yeasts cells into focus. All 25 squares and the cells spread over them are visible at the same time if the low power lens is used (Figure 2). However, cells are easier to visualize with high power (40X) but only one complete square can be seen at a time.

7. **How to Count**:

    a. **Count** the cells in up to five squares systematically – four corner and center (shown in Figure 1a as "R"). Borderline cells should be counted if they lie on the inner and middle of the triple borderlines framing each square. Do not count cells between the middle and the outer borderline (Figure 1b). Record results on Table 2.

    b. **Add** the number of cells in all 5 squares;

    c. **Divide** the total number by 5 to get the average number of cells per square;

    d. **Multiply** the average by 25 for number of cells in all squares and by the **dilution factor** (10 or 100) for the number in original sample;

    e. **Multiply** this number by 10 to arrive at the number of cells in 1μl of original sample.

OBSERVATION AND RESULTS: Table 2

CELL COUNT PER SQUARE					TOTAL No. OF CELLS (Add 1-5)	AVERAGE CELLS/ SQUARE (Divide By 5)	CELLS IN ALL SQUARES (X 25)	DILUTION FACTOR (10 or 100)	CELLS IN ORIGINAL SAMPLE (X DIL. FACTOR)	No. OF CELLS /μl (X 10)	No. OF CELLS/*ml* (X 1000)
1	2	3	4	5							

Final result is expressed in milliliter (μl), which is 1, 000 microliters (μl) and as a factor of 10:

    Estimated Total Cell Count = _____ x 10^(____) CELLS / ml of Suspension

---

Figure 1: Counting Chamber of Etched Slide and Triple-lined Squares (R) with 16 mini-squares

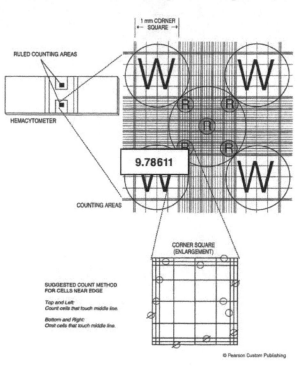

Figure 2: Ruled Counting Area and Central Grid of 25 Triple-lined Squares

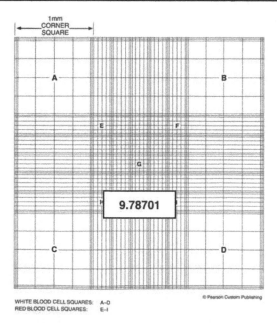

Microbiology of Water

PURPOSES

1. To become familiar with the types of microorganisms present in water.
2. To determine the potability of water using standard qualitative and quantitative procedures.

INTRODUCTION

The importance of potable (drinking) water supplies cannot be overemphasized. With increasing industrialization, water sources available for consumption and recreation have been adulterated with industrial as well as animal and human wastes. As a result, water has become a formidable factor in disease transmission. Polluted waters contain vast amounts of organic matter that serve as excellent nutritional sources for the growth and multiplication of microorganisms. The presence of nonpathogenic organisms is not of major concern, but intestinal contaminants of fecal origin are important. These pathogens are responsible for intestinal infections such as **bacillary dysentery, typhoid fever, cholera,** and **paratyphoid fever**.

Analysis of water samples on a routine basis would not be possible if each pathogen required detection. Therefore water is examined to detect *Escherichia coli*, the bacterium that indicates fecal pollution. Since *E. coli* is always present in the human intestine, its presence in water alerts public health officials to the possible presence of other human or animal intestinal pathogens. Both qualitative and quantitative methods are used to determine the sanitary condition of water.

22

Standard Qualitative Analysis of Water

The three basic tests to detect coliform bacteria in water are presumptive, confirmed, and completed (Figure 1). The tests are performed sequentially on each sample under analysis. They detect the presence of coliform bacteria (indicators of fecal contamination), the gram-negative, non–spore-forming bacilli that ferment lactose with the production of acid and gas that is detectable following a 24-hour incubation period at 37°C.

PART A: Presumptive Test: Determination of the Most Probable Number of Coliform acteria

PURPOSES

1. To determine the presence of coliform bacteria in a water sample.
2. To obtain some index as to the possible number of organisms present in the sample under analysis.

PRINCIPLE

The **presumptive test** is specific for detection of coliform bacteria. Measured aliquots of the water to be tested are added to a lactose fermentation broth containing an inverted gas vial. Because these bacteria are capable of using lactose as a carbon source (the other enteric organisms are not), their detection is facilitated by use of this medium. In this experiment the lactose fermentation broth also contains a surface-tension depressant, bile salt, which is used to suppress the growth of organisms other than coliform bacteria.

Tubes of this lactose medium are inoculated with 10-ml, 1-ml, and 0.1-ml aliquots of the water sample. The series consists of at least three groups, each composed of five tubes of the specified medium. The tubes in each group are then inoculated with the designated volume of the water sample as described under "Procedure." The greater the number of tubes per group, the greater the sensitivity of the test. Development of gas in any of the tubes is *presumptive* evidence of the presence of coliform bacteria in the sample. The presumptive test also enables the microbiologist to obtain some idea of the number of coliform organisms present by means of the **most probable number test (MPN)**. The MPN is estimated by determining the number of tubes in each group that show gas following the incubation period (Table 1).

MATERIALS

Cultures

Water samples from sewage plant, pond, and tap.

Media

Per designated student group: 15 double-strength lactose fermentation broths (LB2X) and 30 single-strength lactose fermentation broths (LB1X).

Equipment

Bunsen burner, 45 test tubes, test-tube rack, sterile 10-ml pipettes, sterile 1-ml pipettes, sterile 0.1ml pipettes, mechanical pipetting device, and glassware marking pencil.

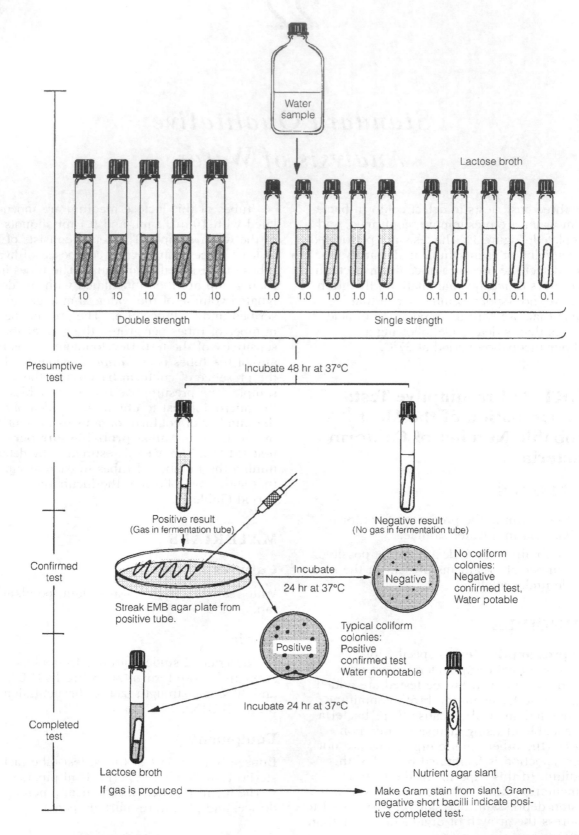

FIGURE 1 Standard method for bacteriological water analysis

TABLE 1 The MPN index per 100 ml for combinations of positive and negative presumptive test results when five 10-ml, five 1-ml, and five 0.1-ml portions of sample are used.

Number of tubes with positive results				Number of tubes with positive results			
Five of 10 ml each	Five of 1 ml each	Five of 0.1 ml each	MPN index per 100 ml	Five of 10 ml each	Five of 1 ml each	Five of 0.1 ml each	MPN index per 100 ml
0	0	0	<2	4	2	1	26
0	0	1	2	4	3	0	27
0	1	0	2	4	3	1	33
0	2	0	4	4	4	0	34
1	0	0	2	5	0	0	23
1	0	1	4	5	0	1	31
1	1	0	4	5	0	2	43
1	1	1	6	5	1	0	33
1	2	0	6	5	1	1	46
2	0	0	5	5	1	2	63
2	0	1	7	5	2	0	49
2	1	0	7	5	2	1	70
2	1	1	9	5	2	2	94
2	2	0	9	5	3	0	79
2	3	0	12	5	3	1	110
3	0	0	8	5	3	2	140
3	0	1	11	5	3	3	180
3	1	0	11	5	4	0	130
3	1	1	14	5	4	1	170
3	2	0	14	5	4	2	220
3	2	1	17	5	4	3	280
3	3	0	17	5	4	4	350
4	0	0	13	5	5	0	240
4	0	1	17	5	5	1	350
4	1	0	17	5	5	2	540
4	1	1	21	5	5	3	920
4	1	2	26	5	5	4	1600
4	2	0	22	5	5	5	≧2400

Source: pp. 9–51, *Standard Methods for the Examination of Water and Wastewater,* 20th Edition (1998). M. J. Taras, A. E. Greenberg, R. D. Hoak, and M. C. Rand, eds. American Public Health Association, Washington, D. C. Copyright 1998, American Public Health Association.

PROCEDURE ⚠

1. Set up three separate series consisting of three groups, a total of 15 tubes per series, in a test-tube rack; for each tube, label the water source and volume of sample inoculated as illustrated.

Series 1: Sewage water	5 tubes of LB2X-10 ml 5 tubes of LB1X-1 ml 5 tubes of LB1X-0.1 ml
Series 2: Pond water	5 tubes of LB2X-10 ml 5 tubes of LB1X-1 ml 5 tubes of LB1X-0.1 ml
Series 3: Tap water	5 tubes of LB2X-10 ml 5 tubes of LB1X-1 ml 5 tubes of LB1X-0.1 ml

178

2. Mix sewage plant water sample by shaking thoroughly. **Exercise care in handling sewage waste water sample because enteric pathogens may be present.**

3. Flame bottle and then, using a 10-ml pipette, transfer 10-ml aliquots of water sample to the five tubes labeled LB2X-10 ml.

4. Flame bottle and then, using a 1-ml pipette, transfer 1-ml aliquots of water sample to the five tubes labeled LB1X-1 ml.

5. Flame bottle and then, using a 0.1-ml pipette, transfer 0.1-ml aliquots of water sample to the five tubes labeled LB1X-0.1 ml.

6. Repeat Steps 2 through 5 for the tap and pond water samples.

7. Incubate all tubes for 48 hours at 37°C.

PART B: Confirmed Test

PURPOSE

To co   the presence of coliform bacteria in a water sample for which the presumptive test was positive.

PRINCIPLE

The presence of a positive or doubtful presumptive test immediately suggests that the water sample is nonpotable. Confirmation of these results is necessary, since positive presumptive tests may be the result of organisms of noncoliform origin that are not recognized as indicators of fecal pollution.

The **confirmed test** requires that selective and differential media such as eosin–methylene blue (EMB) or endo agar be streaked from a positive lactose broth tube obtained from the presumptive test. The nature of differential and selective media was discussed in Experiment 14 but is reviewed briefly here. Eosin–methylene blue contains the dye methylene blue, which inhibits the growth of gram-positive organisms. In the presence of an acid environment, EMB forms a complex that precipitates out onto the coliform colonies, producing dark centers and a green metallic sheen. This reaction is characteristic for *Escherichia coli*, the major

indicator of fecal pollution. Endo agar is a nutrient medium containing the dye fuchsin, which is present in the decolorized state. In the presence of acid produced by the coliform bacteria, fuchsin forms a dark pink complex that turns the *E. coli* colonies and the surrounding medium pink.

MATERIALS

Cultures

One 24-hour-old positive lactose broth culture from each of the three series from the presumptive test.

Media

Three each per designated student group: Eosin–methylene blue agar plates or endo agar plates.

Equipment

Bunsen burner, glassware marking pencil, and inoculating loop.

PROCEDURE

1. Label the covers of the three EMB plates or the three endo agar plates with the source of the water sample (sewage, pond, and tap).

2. Using a positive 24-hour lactose broth culture from the sewage water series from the presumptive test, streak the surface of one EMB or one endo agar plate, as described in Experiment 2, to obtain discrete colonies.

3. Repeat Step 2 using the positive lactose broth cultures from the pond and tap water series to inoculate the remaining plates.

4. Incubate all plate cultures in an inverted position for 24 hours at 37°C.

PART C: Completed Test

PURPOSE

To confirm the presence of coliform bacteria in a water sample, or, if necessary, to confirm a suspicious but doubtful result of the previous test.

Standard Qualitative Analysis of Water

PRINCIPLE

The **completed test** is the final analysis of the water sample. It is used to examine the coliform colonies that appeared on the EMB or endo agar plates used in the confirmed test. An isolated colony is picked from the confirmatory test plate and inoculated into a tube of lactose broth and streaked on a nutrient agar slant to perform a Gram stain. Following inoculation and incubation, tubes showing acid and gas in the lactose broth and the presence of gram-negative bacilli on microscopic examination are further confirmation of the presence of *E. coli*, and they are indicative of a positive completed test.

MATERIALS

Cultures

One 24-hour coliform-positive EMB or endo agar culture from each of the three series of the confirmed test.

Media

Three each per designated student group: nutrient agar slants and lactose fermentation broths.

Reagents

Crystal violet, Gram's iodine, 95% ethyl alcohol, and safranin.

Equipment

Bunsen burner, staining tray, inoculating loop, lens paper, bibulous paper, microscope, and glassware marking pencil.

PROCEDURE

1. Label each tube with the source of its water sample.
2. Inoculate one lactose broth and one nutrient agar slant from the same isolated *E. coli* colony obtained from an EMB or an endo agar plate from each of the experimental water samples.
3. Incubate all tubes for 24 hours at 37°C.

Name   Section   Date

OBSERVATIONS AND RESULTS

PART A: Presumptive Test

1. Examine all tubes after 24 and 48 hours of incubation. Record your results in the chart as:
   a. Positive: 10% or more of gas appears in a tube in 24 hours.
   b. Doubtful: Gas develops in a tube after 48 hours.
   c. Negative: There is no gas in a tube after 48 hours.
2. Determine and record the MPN using Table 1.

✚ *Refer to the color-plate insert for illustration of these reactions.*

Example: If gas appeared in all five tubes labeled LB2X-10, in two of the tubes labeled LB1X-1, and in one labeled LB1X-0.1, the series would be read as 5-2-1. From the MPN table, such a reading would indicate that there would be approximately 150 microorganisms per 100 ml of water, with a 95% probability that there are between 30 and 440 microorganisms present.

	Gas															Reading	MPN	Range 95% Probability
	LB2X-10					LB1X-1					LB1X-0.1							
	Tube					Tube					Tube							
Water Sample	1	2	3	4	5	1	2	3	4	5	1	2	3	4	5			
Sewage																		
Pond																		
Tap																		

PART B: Confirmed Test

1. Examine all the plates for the presence or absence of *E. coli* colonies. Record your results in the chart.

✚ *Refer to the color-plate insert for an illustration of E. coli growth on an EMB plate.*

2. Based on your results, determine and record whether each of the samples is potable or nonpotable. The presence of *E. coli* is a positive confirmed test, indicating that the water is nonpotable. The absence of *E. coli* is a negative test, indicating that the water is not contaminated with fecal wastes and is therefore potable.

Water Sample	Coliforms		Potable	Nonpotable
	EMB Plate	Endo Agar Plate		
Sewage				
Pond				
Tap				

Standard Qualitative Analysis of Water

PART C: Completed Test

1. Examine all lactose fermentation broth cultures for the presence or absence of acid and gas. Record your results in the chart.
2. Prepare a Gram stain, using the nutrient agar slant cultures of the organisms that showed a positive result in the lactose fermentation broth.
3. Examine the slides microscopically for the presence of gram-negative short bacilli, which are indicative of *E. coli* and thus nonpotable water. Record your results for Gram stain reaction and morphology of the cells in the chart.

Water Source	Lactose Broth A/G (+) or (−)	Gram Stain	Potability	
		Reaction/Morphology	Potable	Nonpotable
Sewage				
Pond				
Tap				

REVIEW QUESTIONS

1. What is the rationale for selecting *E. coli* as the indicator of water potability?

2. Why is this procedure qualitative rather than quantitative?

3. Explain why it is of prime importance to analyze water supplies that serve industrialized communities.

4. Account for the presence of microorganisms in natural bodies of water and sewage systems. What is their function? Explain.

Biochemical Activities
of Microorganisms

PURPOSES

This section is designed to instruct you in
1. The nature and activities of exoenzymes and endoenzymes.
2. Experimental procedures for differentiation of enteric microorganisms.
3. Biochemical test procedures for identification of microorganisms.

INTRODUCTION

Microorganisms must be separated and identified for a wide variety of reasons, such as:

1. Determination of pathogens responsible for infectious diseases.
2. Selection and isolation of strains of fermentative microorganisms necessary for the industrial production of alcohols, solvents, vitamins, organic acids, antibiotics, and industrial enzymes.
3. Isolation and development of suitable microbial strains necessary for the manufacture and the enhancement of quality and flavor in certain food materials such as yogurt, cheeses, and other milk products.
4. Comparison of biochemical activities for taxonomic purposes.

To accomplish these tasks, the microbiologist is assisted by the fact that, just as human beings possess a characteristic and specific set of fingerprints, microorganisms all have their own identifying biochemical characteristics. These so-called biochemical fingerprints are the properties controlled by the cells' enzymatic activity, and they are responsible for bioenergetics, biosynthesis, and biodegradation.

The sum of all these chemical reactions is defined as **cellular metabolism**, and the biochemical transformations that occur both outside and inside the cell are governed by biological catalysts called **enzymes**.

Extracellular Enzymes (Exoenzymes)

Exoenzymes act on substances outside of the cell. Most high-molecular-weight substances are not able to pass through cell membranes and therefore these raw materials—foodstuffs such as polysaccharides, lipids, and proteins—must be degraded to low-molecular-weight materials—nutrients—before they can be transported into the

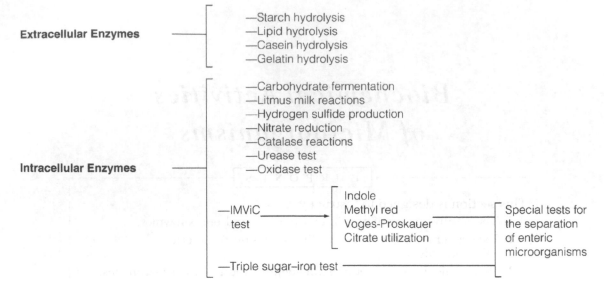

FIGURE 1 Biochemical activities of microorganisms

cell. Because of the reactions involved, exoenzymes are mainly **hydrolytic enzymes** that reduce high-molecular-weight materials into their building blocks by introducing water into the molecule. This liberates smaller molecules, which may then be transported into the cell and assimilated.

Intracellular Enzymes (Endoenzymes)

Exoenzymes function inside the cell and are mainly responsible for synthesis of new protoplasmic requirements and production of cellular energy from assimilated materials. The ability of cells to act on nutritional substrates permeating cell membranes indicates the presence of many endoenzymes capable of transforming the chemically specific substrates into essential materials.

This transformation is necessary for cellular survival and function, and it is the basis of cellular metabolism. As a result of these metabolic processes, metabolic products are formed and excreted by the cell into the environment. Assay of these end products not only aids in identification of specific enzyme systems but also serves to identify, separate, and classify microorganisms. Figure 1 represents a simplified schema of experimental procedures used to acquaint students with the intracellular and extracellular enzymatic activities of microorganisms.

The experiments you will carry out in this section can be performed in either of two ways. A short version uses a limited number of organisms to illustrate the possible end product(s) that may result from enzyme action on a substrate. The organisms for this version are designated in the individual exercises.

The alternative, or long, version involves the use of 13 microorganisms. This version provides a complete overview of the biochemical fingerprints of the organisms and supplies the format for their separation and identification. These organisms were chosen to serve as a basis for identification of an unknown microorganism. If this alternative version is selected, the following organisms are recommended for use:

Escherichia coli   *Alcaligenes faecalis*
Enterobacter aerogenes   *Micrococcus luteus*
Klebsiella pneumoniae   *Streptococcus lactis*
Shigella dysenteriae   *Staphylococcus aureus*
Salmonella typhimurium   *Bacillus cereus*
Proteus vulgaris   *Corynebacterim xerosis*
Pseudomonas aeruginosa

23

Carbohydrate Fermentation

PURPOSE

To determine the ability of microorganisms to degrade and ferment carbohydrates with the production of an acid or acid and gas.

PRINCIPLE

Most microorganisms obtain their energy through a series of orderly and integrated enzymatic reactions leading to the biooxidation of a substrate, frequently a carbohydrate. The major pathways by which this is accomplished are shown in Figure 1.

Organisms use carbohydrates differently depending on their enzyme complement. Some organisms are capable of fermenting sugars such as glucose anaerobically, while others use the aerobic pathway. Still others, facultative anaerobes, are enzymatically competent to use both aerobic and anaerobic pathways, and some organisms lack the ability to oxidize glucose by either. In this exercise the fermentative pathways are of prime concern.

In fermentation, substrates such as carbohydrates and alcohols undergo anaerobic dissimilation and produce an organic acid (for example, lactic, formic, or acetic acid) that may be accompanied by gases such as hydrogen or carbon dioxide. Facultative anaerobes are usually the so-called fermenters of carbohydrates. Fermentation is best described by considering the degradation of glucose by way of the **Embden-Meyerhof pathway**, also known as the **glycolytic pathway**, illustrated in Figure 2.

As the diagram shows, one mole of glucose is converted into two moles of pyruvic acid, which is the major intermediate compound produced by glucose degradation. Subsequent metabolism of pyruvate is not the same for all organisms, and a variety of end products result that define their different fermentative capabilities. This can be seen in Figure 3.

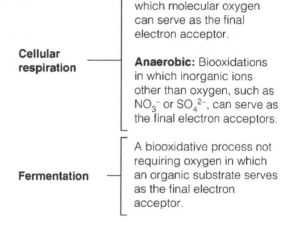

Cellular respiration

- **Aerobic:** Biooxidations in which molecular oxygen can serve as the final electron acceptor.
- **Anaerobic:** Biooxidations in which inorganic ions other than oxygen, such as NO_3^- or SO_4^{2-}, can serve as the final electron acceptors.

Fermentation — A biooxidative process not requiring oxygen in which an organic substrate serves as the final electron acceptor.

FIGURE 1 Biooxidative pathways

Fermentative degradation under anaerobic conditions is carried out in a fermentation broth tube containing a Durham tube, an inverted inner vial for the detection of gas production as illustrated in Figure 4. A typical carbohydrate fermentation medium contains

1. Nutrient broth ingredients for the support of the growth of all organisms.
2. A specific carbohydrate that serves as the substrate for determining the organism's fermentative capabilities.
3. The pH indicator phenol red, which is red at a neutral pH (7) and changes to yellow at a slightly acidic pH of 6.8, indicating that slight amounts of acid will cause a color change.

The critical nature of the fermentation reaction and the activity of the indicator make it imperative that all cultures should be observed within 48 hours. Extended incubation may mask acid-producing reactions by production of alkali because of enzymatic action on substrates other than the carbohydrate.

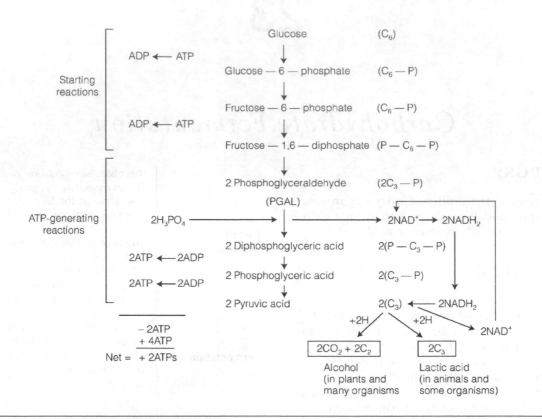

FIGURE 2   The Embden-Meyerhof pathway

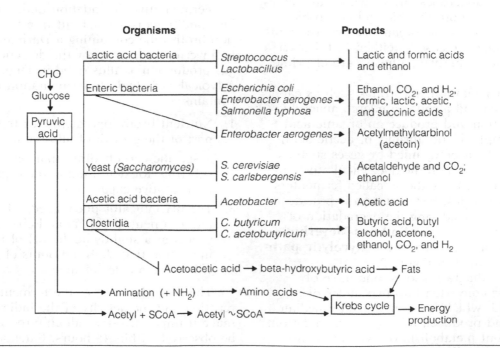

FIGURE 3   Variations in the use of pyruvic acid

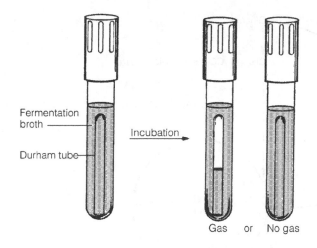

Fermentation broth

Durham tube

Incubation →

Gas   or   No gas

FIGURE 4   Detection of gas production

Following incubation, carbohydrates that have been fermented with the production of acidic wastes will cause the phenol red to turn yellow, thereby indicating a positive reaction. In some cases, acid production is accompanied by the evolution of a gas (CO_2) that will be visible as a bubble in the inverted tube. Cultures that are not capable fermenting a carbohydrate substrate will ...ot change the indicator, and the tubes will appear red; there will not be a concomitant evolution of gas. This is a negative reaction.

The lack of carbohydrate fermentation by some organisms should not be construed as absence of growth. The organisms use other nutrients in the medium as energy sources. Among these nutrients are peptones present in nutrient broth. Peptones can be degraded by microbial enzymes to amino acids that are in turn enzymatically converted by oxidative deamination to ketoamino acids. These are then metabolized through the Krebs cycle for energy production. These reactions liberate ammonia, which accumulates in the medium, forming ammonium hydroxide (NH_4OH) and producing an alkaline environment. When this occurs, the phenol red turns to a deep red in the now basic medium. This alternative pathway of aerobic respiration is illustrated in Figure 5.

MATERIALS

Cultures

24- to 48-hour trypticase soy broth cultures of *Escherichia coli*, *Alcaligenes faecalis*, *Salmonella typhimurium*, and *Staphylococcus aureus* for the short version. 24- to 48-hour trypticase soy broth cultures of the 13 previously listed organisms for the long version.

Media

Per designated student group: phenol red lactose, dextrose (glucose), and sucrose broths: five of each for the short version, 14 of each for the long version.

Equipment

Bunsen burner, inoculating loop, and glassware marking pencil.

PROCEDURE

1. Using sterile technique, inoculate each experimental organism into its appropriately labeled medium by means of loop inoculation. **Take care during this step not to shake the fermentation tube**; shaking the tube may accidentally force a bubble of air into the inverted gas vial, displacing the medium and possibly rendering a false positive result. The last tube will serve as a control.
2. Incubate all tubes for 24 hours at 37°C.

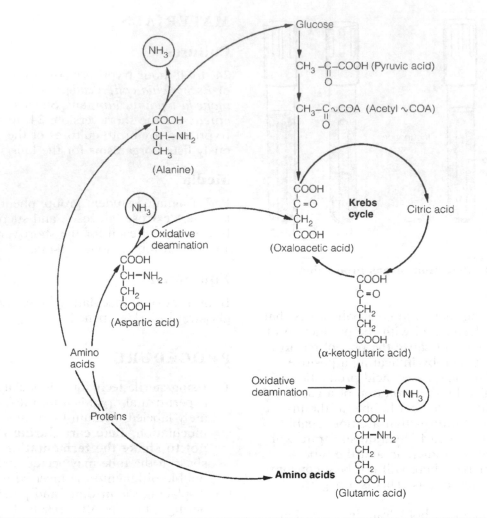

FIGURE 5 Proteins as energy sources for microbes

Carbohydrate Fermentation

Name   Section   Date

OBSERVATIONS AND RESULTS

1. Examine all carbohydrate broth cultures for color and the presence or absence of a gas bubble. Record your results in the chart.
2. Based on your observations, determine and record whether or not each organism was capable of fermenting the carbohydrate substrate with the production of acid or acid and gas.

✚ *Refer to the color-plate insert for illustration of these reactions.*

Bacterial Species	Lactose Observation (color of medium, bubble in fermentation tube)	Result (A), (A/G), or (−)	Dextrose Observation (color of medium, bubble in fermentation tube)	Result (A), (A/G), or (−)	Sucrose Observation (color of medium, bubble in fermentation tube)	Result (A), (A/G), or (−)
E. coli						
E. aerogenes						
K. pneumoniae						
S. dysenteriae						
S. typhimurium						
' vulgaris						
P. aeruginosa						
A. faecalis						
M. luteus						
S. lactis						
S. aureus						
B. cereus						
C. xerosis						
Control						

REVIEW QUESTIONS

1. Distinguish between respiration and fermentation.

2. Do all microorganisms use pyruvic acid in the same way? Explain.

3. Describe a pathway used for the degradation of carbohydrates by strict anaerobes.

4. 🔍 From your experimental data, you know that *P. aeruginosa* did not utilize any of the carbohydrates in the test media. In view of this, how do these organisms generate energy to sustain their viability?

5. 🔍 *Clostridium perfringens*, an obligate anaerobe, is capable of utilizing the carbohydrates released from injured tissues as an energy source. During the infectious process, large amounts of gas accumulate in the infected tissues. Would you expect this gas to be CO_2? Explain.

24

Extracellular Enzymatic Activities of Microorganisms

PURPOSE

To determine the ability of microorganisms to excrete hydrolytic extracellular enzymes capable of degrading the polysaccharide starch, the lipid tributyrin, and the proteins casein and gelatin.

PRINCIPLE

Because of their large sizes, high-molecular-weight nutrients such as polysaccharides, lipids, and proteins are not capable of permeating the cell membrane. These macromolecules must first be hydrolyzed by ecific extracellular enzymes into their spective basic building blocks. These low-molecular-weight substances can then be transported into the cells and used for the synthesis of protoplasmic requirements and energy production. The following procedures are designed to investigate the exoenzymatic activities of different microorganisms.

Starch Hydrolysis

Starch is a high-molecular-weight, branching polymer composed of **glucose** molecules linked together by **glycosidic bonds**. The degradation of this macromolecule first requires the presence of the extracellular enzyme **amylase** for its hydrolysis into shorter polysaccharides, namely **dextrins**, and ultimately into **maltose** molecules. The final hydrolysis of this disaccharide, which is catalyzed by **maltase**, yields low-molecular-weight, soluble **glucose** molecules that can be transported into the cell and used for energy production through the process of glycolysis.

In this experimental procedure, starch agar is used to demonstrate the hydrolytic activities of these exoenzymes. The medium is composed of nutrient agar supplemented with starch, which serves as the polysaccha-

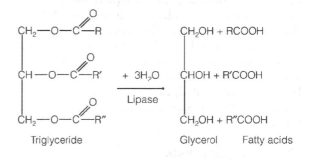

FIGURE 1 Lipid hydrolysis

ride substrate. The detection of the hydrolytic activity following the growth period is made by performing the starch test to determine the presence or absence of starch in the medium. Starch in the presence of iodine will impart a blue-black color to the medium, indicating the absence of starch-splitting enzymes and representing a negative result. If the starch has been hydrolyzed, a clear zone of hydrolysis will surround the growth of the organism. This is a positive result.

Lipid Hydrolysis

Lipids are high-molecular-weight compounds possessing large amounts of energy. The degradation of lipids such as **triglycerides** is accomplished by extracellular hydrolyzing enzymes, called **lipases** (esterases), that cleave the **ester bonds** in this molecule by the addition of water to form the building blocks **glycerol** (an alcohol) and **fatty acids**. Figure 1 shows this reaction. Once assimilated into the cell, these basic components can be further metabolized through aerobic respiration to produce cellular energy, adenosine triphosphate (ATP). The components may also enter other metabolic pathways for the synthesis of other cellular protoplasmic requirements.

In this experimental procedure, tributyrin agar is used to demonstrate the hydrolytic activities of the exoenzyme lipase. The medium is composed of nutrient agar supplemented with the triglyceride tributyrin as the lipid substrate. Tributyrin forms an emulsion when dispersed in the agar, producing an opaque medium that is necessary for observing exoenzymatic activity.

Following inoculation and incubation of the agar plate cultures, organisms excreting lipase will show a zone of **lipolysis**, which is demonstrated by a clear area surrounding the bacterial growth. This loss of opacity is the result of the hydrolytic reaction yielding soluble glycerol and fatty acids and represents a positive reaction for lipid hydrolysis. In the absence of lipolytic enzymes, the medium retains its opacity. This is a negative reaction.

Casein Hydrolysis

Casein, the major milk protein, is a macromolecule composed of **amino acid** subunits linked together by **peptide bonds** (CO—NH). Before their assimilation into the cell, proteins must undergo step-by-step degradation into p   1es, **polypeptides**, **dipeptides**, and u........ely into their building blocks, **amino acids**. This process is called peptonization, or **proteolysis**, and it is mediated by extracellular enzymes called **proteases**. The function of these proteases is to cleave the peptide bond CO—NH by introducing water into the molecule. The reaction then liberates the amino acids, as illustrated in Figure 2.

The low-molecular-weight soluble amino acids can now be transported through the cell membrane into the intracellular amino acid pool for use in the synthesis of structural and functional cellular proteins.

In this experimental procedure, milk agar is used to demonstrate the hydrolytic activity of these exoenzymes. The medium is composed of nutrient agar supplemented with milk that contains the protein substrate casein. Similar to other proteins, milk protein is a colloidal suspension that gives the medium its color and opacity, because it deflects light rays rather than transmitting them.

Following inoculation and incubation of the agar plate cultures, organisms secreting proteases will exhibit a zone of proteolysis, which is demonstrated by a clear area

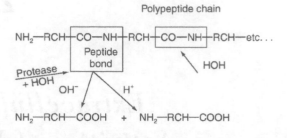

FIGURE 2 Protein hydrolysis

surrounding the bacterial growth. This loss of opacity is the result of a hydrolytic reaction yielding soluble, noncolloidal amino acids, and it represents a positive reaction. In the absence of protease activity, the medium surrounding the growth of the organism remains opaque, which is a negative reaction.

Gelatin Hydrolysis

Although the value of gelatin as a nutritional source is questionable (it is an incomplete protein, lacking the essential amino acid tryptophan), its value in identifying bacterial species is well-established. Gelatin is a protein produced by hydrolysis of collagen, a major component of connective tissue and tendons in humans and other animals. Below temperatures of 25°C, gelatin will maintain its gel properties and exist as a solid; at temperatures above 25°C, gelatin is liquid.

Liquefaction is accomplished by some microorganisms capable of producing a proteolytic extracellular enzyme called **gelatinase**, which acts to hydrolyze this protein to **amino acids**. Once this degradation occurs, even very low temperatures of 4°C will not restore the gel characteristic.

In this experimental procedure, you will use nutrient gelatin deep tubes to demonstrate the hydrolytic activity of gelatinase. The medium consists of nutrient broth supplemented with 12% gelatin. This high gelatin concentration results in a stiff medium and also serves as the substrate for the activity of gelatinase.

Following inoculation and incubation for 48 hours, the cultures are placed in a refrigerator at 4°C for 30 minutes. Cultures that remain liquefied produce gelatinase and demonstrate **rapid** gelatin hydrolysis. Reincubate all solidified cultures for an additional 5 days. Refrigerate for 30 minutes and observe for liquefaction. Cultures that remain liquefied are indicative of **slow** gelatin hydrolysis.

MATERIALS

Cultures

24- to 48-hour trypticase soy broth cultures of *Escherichia coli, Bacillus cereus, Pseudomonas aeruginosa,* and *Staphylococcus aureus* for the short version. 24- to 48-hour trypticase soy broth cultures of the 13 previously listed organisms for the long version.

Media

Short version: Two plates each of starch agar, tributyrin agar, and milk agar, and three nutrient gelatin deep tubes per designated student group. Long version: Four plates each of starch agar, tributyrin agar, and milk agar, and 14 nutrient gelatin deep tubes per designated student group.

Reagent

Gram's iodine solution.

Equipment

Bunsen burner, inoculating loop and needle, glassware marking pencil, test tube rack, and refrigerator.

PROCEDURE

1. Prepare the starch agar, tributyrin agar, and milk agar plates for inoculation as follows:
   a. Short procedure: Using two plates per medium, divide the bottom of each Petri dish into two sections. Label the sections as *E. coli, B. cereus, P. aeruginosa,* and *S. aureus,* respectively.
   b. Long procedure: Repeat Step 1a, dividing three plate bottoms into three sections and one plate bottom into four sections for each of the required media, to accommodate the 13 test organisms.
2. Using sterile technique, make a single-line streak inoculation of each test organism on the agar surface of its appropriately labeled section on the agar plates.
3. Using sterile technique, inoculate each experimental organism in its appropriately labeled gelatin deep tube by means of a stab inoculation.
4. Incubate all plates in an inverted position for 24 to 48 hours at 37°C. Incubate the gelatin deep tube cultures for 48 hours. Re-incubate all negative cultures for an additional 5 days.

Name   Section   Date

OBSERVATIONS AND RESULTS

Starch Hydrolysis

1. Flood the starch agar plate cultures with Gram's iodine solution, allow the iodine to remain in contact with the medium for 30 seconds, and pour off the excess.
2. Examine the cultures for the presence or absence of a blue-black color surrounding the growth of each test organism. Record your results in the chart.
3. Based on your observations, determine and record which organisms were capable of hydrolyzing the starch.

✚ *Refer to the color-plate insert for illustration of these reactions.*

Lipid Hydrolysis

1. Examine the tributyrin agar plate cultures for the presence or absence of a clear area, or zone of lipolysis, surrounding the growth of each of the organisms. Record your results in the chart.
2. Based on your observations, determine and record which organisms were capable of hydrolyzing the lipid.

✚ *Refer to the color-plate insert for illustration of these reactions.*

Bacterial Species	Starch Hydrolysis		Tributyrin Hydrolysis	
	Appearance of Medium	Result (+) or (−)	Appearance of Medium	Result (+) or (−)
E. coli				
E. aerogenes				
K. pneumoniae				
S. dysenteriae				
S. typhimurium				
P. vulgaris				
P. aeruginosa				
A. faecalis				
M. luteus				
S. lactis				
S. aureus				
B. cereus				
C. xerosis				

Extracellular Enzymatic Activities of Microorganisms

Casein Hydrolysis

1. Examine the milk agar plate cultures for the presence or absence of a clear area, or zone of proteolysis, surrounding the growth of each of the bacterial test organisms. Record your results in the chart.
2. Based on your observations, determine and record which of the organisms were capable of hydrolyzing the milk protein casein.

Gelatin Hydrolysis

1. Place all gelatin deep tube cultures into a refrigerator at 4°C for 30 minutes.
2. Examine all the cultures to determine whether the medium is solid or liquid. Record your results in the chart.
3. Based on your observations following the 2-day and 7-day incubation periods, determine and record (a) which organisms were capable of hydrolyzing gelatin and (b) the rate of hydrolysis.

Bacterial Species	Casein Hydrolysis		Gelatin Hydrolysis		
	Appearance of Medium	Result (+) or (−)	Liquefaction (+) or (−)		Rate of Hydrolysis (Slow or Rapid)
			2 days	7 days	
E. coli					
E. aerogenes					
K. pneu					
S. dysenteriae					
S. typhimurium					
P. vulgaris					
P. aeruginosa					
A. faecalis					
M. luteus					
S. lactis					
S. aureus					
B. cereus					
C. xerosis					

Extracellular Enzymatic Activities of Microorganisms

25

Nitrate Reduction Test

PURPOSE

To determine the ability of some microorganisms to reduce nitrates (NO_3^-) to nitrites (NO_2^-) or beyond the nitrite stage.

PRINCIPLE

The reduction of nitrates by some aerobic and facultative anaerobic microorganisms occurs in the absence of molecular oxygen, an anaerobic process. In these organisms anaerobic respiration is an oxidative process whereby the cell uses inorganic substances such as nitrates (NO_3^-) or sulfates (SO_4^{2-}) to supply oxygen that is subsequently utilized as a final hydrogen acceptor during energy formation. The biochemical transformation may be visualized as follows:

$$NO_3^- + 2H^+ + 2e \xrightarrow{\text{Nitrate Reductase}} NO_2^- + H_2O$$

Nitrate   **Hydrogen electrons**   **Nitrite**   **Water**

Some organisms possess the enzymatic capacity to act further on nitrites to reduce them to ammonia (NH_3^+) or molecular nitrogen (N_2). These reactions may be described as follows:

$$NO_2^- \longrightarrow NH_3^+$$

Nitrite   **Ammonia**

or

$$2NO_3^- + 12H^+ + 10e^- \longrightarrow N_2 + 6H_2O$$

Nitrate   **Molecular nitrogen**

Nitrate reduction can be determined by cultivating organisms in a nitrate broth medium. The medium is basically a nutrient broth supplemented with 0.1% potassium nitrate (KNO_3) as the nitrate substrate. In addition, the medium is made into a semisolid by the addition of 0.1% agar. The semisolidity impedes the diffusion of oxygen into the medium, thereby favoring the anaerobic requirement necessary for nitrate reduction.

Following incubation of the cultures, an organism's ability to reduce nitrates to nitrites is determined by the addition of two reagents: Solution A, which is sulfanilic acid, followed by Solution B, which is alpha-naphthylamine. Following reduction, the addition of Solutions A and B will produce an immediate cherry red color.

$$NO_3^- \xrightarrow{\text{Nitrate Reductase}} NO_2^- \text{ (Red color on addition of Solutions A and B)}$$

Cultures not producing a color change suggest one of two possibilities: (1) nitrates were not reduced by the organism, or (2) the organism possessed such potent **nitrate reductase** enzymes that nitrates were rapidly reduced beyond nitrites to ammonia or even molecular nitrogen. To determine whether or not nitrates were reduced past the nitrite stage, a small amount of zinc powder is added to the basically colorless cultures already containing Solutions A and B. Zinc reduces nitrates to nitrites. The development of red color therefore verifies that nitrates were not reduced to nitrites by the organism. If nitrates were not reduced, a negative nitrate reduction reaction has occurred. If the addition of zinc does not produce a color change, the nitrates in the medium were reduced beyond nitrites to ammonia or nitrogen gas. This is a positive reaction, as shown in Figure 1.

MATERIALS

Cultures

24- to 48-hour trypticase soy broth cultures of *Escherichia coli*, *Alcaligenes faecalis*, and *Pseudomonas aeruginosa* for the short version. 24- to 48-hour trypticase soy broth cultures of the 13 previously listed organisms for the long version.

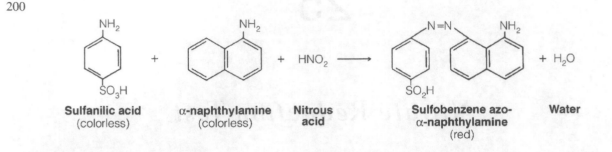

FIGURE 1 Formation of colored complex indicative of NO₃⁻ reduction

Media

Trypticase nitrate broth per designated student group: four for the short version, 14 for the long version.

Reagents

Solution A (sulfanilic acid), Solution B (alpha-naphthylamine), and zinc powder.

Equipment

Bunsen burner, inoculating loop, test tube rack, and glassware marking pencil.

PROCEDURE

1. Using sterile technique, inoculate each experimental organism into its appropriately labeled tube by means of a loop inoculation. The last tube will serve as a control.

2. Incubate all cultures for 24 to 48 hours at 37°C.

Name   Section   Date

OBSERVATIONS AND RESULTS

1. Add five drops of Solution A and then five drops of Solution B to all nitrate broth cultures. Observe and record in the chart whether or not a red coloration develops in each of the cultures.

2. Add a minute quantity of zinc to the cultures in which no red color developed. Observe and record whether or not red coloration develops in each of the cultures.

3. On the basis of your observations, determine and record whether or not each organism was capable of nitrate reduction. Identify the end product (NO_2^- or NH_3^+/N_2), if any, that is present.

✚ *Refer to the color-plate insert for illustration of these reactions.*

Bacterial Species	Red Coloration with Solutions A and B (+) or (−)	Red Coloration with Zinc (+) or (−)	Nitrate Reduction (+) or (−)	End Products
E. coli				
E. aerogenes				
K. pneumoniae				
S. dysenteriae				
. typhimurium				
P. vulgaris				
P. aeruginosa				
A. faecalis				
M. luteus				
S. lactis				
S. aureus				
B. cereus				
C. xerosis				
Control				

REVIEW QUESTIONS

1. Explain the function of the 0.1% agar in the nitrate medium.

Nitrate Reduction Test

202

2. Explain the functions of Solutions A and B.

3. If a culture does not undergo a color change on the addition of Solutions A and B, explain how you would interpret this result.

4. Explain why the development of a red color on the addition of zinc is a negative test.

5. Discuss the relationship between an organism's ability to reduce nitrate past the nitrite stage and that organism's proteolytic activity.

Nitrate Reduction Test

26

IMViC Test

Identification of enteric bacilli is of prime importance in controlling intestinal infections by preventing contamination of food and water supplies. The groups of bacteria that can be found in the intestinal tract of humans and lower mammals are classified as members of the family **Enterobacteriaceae**. They are short, gram-negative, nonspore-forming bacilli. Included in this family are

1. **Pathogens** such as members of the genera *Salmonella* and *Shigella*.
2. **Occasional pathogens** such as members of the genera *Proteus* and *Klebsiella*.
3. **Normal intestinal flora** such as members of the genera *Escherichia* and *Enterobacter*, which are saprophytic inhabitants of the intestinal tract.

Differentiation of the principal groups of Enterobacteriaceae can be accomplished on the basis of their biochemical properties and enzymatic reactions in the presence of specific substrates. The **IMViC** series of tests (**indole, methyl-red, Voges-Proskauer,** and **citrate utilization**) can be used.

The following experiments are designed for either a short or long version. The short version uses selected members of the enteric family. The long procedure makes use of bacterial species that do not belong solely to the Enterobacteriaceae. Nonenteric forms are included to acquaint you with the biochemical activities of other organisms grown in these media and to enable you to use these data for further comparisons of both types of bacteria. Selected organisms to be used in the long-version procedures are listed. The enteric organisms are subdivided as lactose fermenters and nonfermenters.

Escherichia coli
Enterobacter aerogenes } **Lactose fermenters**
Klebsiella pneumoniae

Salmonella typhimurium
Shigella dysenteriae
Proteus vulgaris } **Lactose nonfermenters**
Pseudomonas aeruginosa
Alcaligenes faecalis

} **Enteric**

Corynebacterium xerosis
Micrococcus luteus
Streptococcus lactis } **Nonenteric**
Staphylococcus aureus
Bacillus cereus

Figure 7 shows the biochemical reactions that occur during the IMViC tests. It is designed to assist you in the execution and interpretation of each test.

PART A: Indole Production Test

PURPOSE

To determine the ability of microorganisms to degrade the amino acid tryptophan.

PRINCIPLE

Tryptophan is an essential amino acid that can undergo oxidation by way of the enzymatic activities of some bacteria. Conversion of tryptophan into metabolic products is mediated by the enzyme **tryptophanase**.

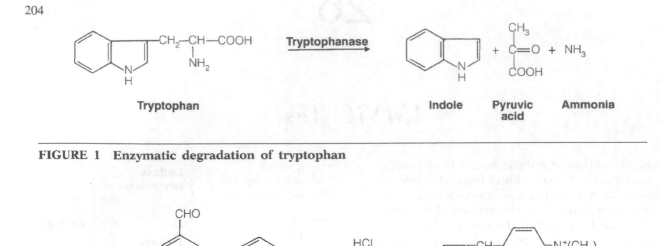

FIGURE 1   Enzymatic degradation of tryptophan

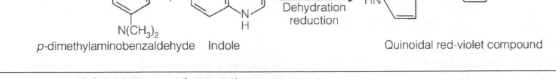

FIGURE 2   Indole reaction with Kovac's reagent

This reaction is illustrated in Figure 1. This ability to hydrolyze tryptophan with the production of indole is not a characteristic of all microorganisms and therefore serves as a biochemical marker.

In this experiment, SIM agar, which contains the substrate tryptophan, is used. The presence of indole is detectable by adding Kovac's reagent, which produces a cherry red reagent layer. This color is produced by the reagent, which is composed of *p*-dimethylaminobenzaldehyde, butanol, and hydrochloric acid. Indole is extracted from the medium into the reagent layer by the acidified butyl alcohol component and forms a complex with the *p*-dimethylaminobenzaldehyde, yielding the cherry red color. This reaction is illustrated in Figure 2.

Cultures producing a red reagent layer following addition of Kovac's reagent are indole-positive. The absence of red coloration demonstrates that the substrate tryptophan was not hydrolyzed and indicates an indole-negative reaction.

MATERIALS

Cultures

24- to 48-hour trypticase soy broth cultures of *Escherichia coli*, *Proteus vulgaris*, and *Enterobacter aerogenes* for the short version.

24- to 48-hour trypticase soy broth cultures of the 13 previously listed organisms for the long version.

Media

SIM agar deep tubes per designated student group: four for the short version, 14 for the long version.

Reagent

Kovac's reagent.

Equipment

Bunsen burner, inoculating needle, test tube rack, and glassware marking pencil.

PROCEDURE

1. Using sterile technique, inoculate each experimental organism into its appropriately labeled deep tube by means of a stab inoculation. The last tube will serve as a control.

2. Incubate tubes for 24 to 48 hours at 37°C.

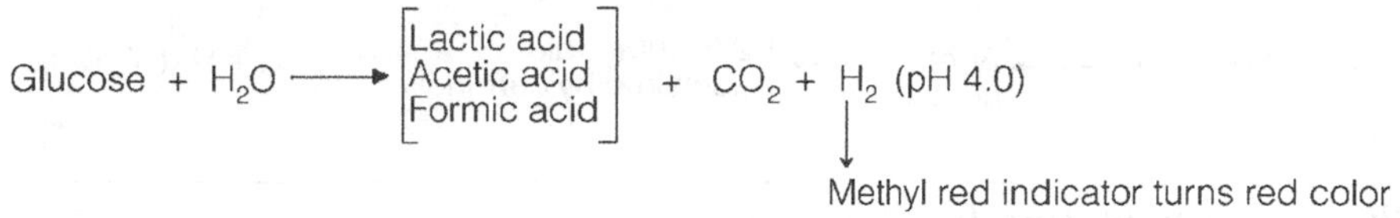

$$\text{Glucose} + H_2O \longrightarrow \begin{bmatrix} \text{Lactic acid} \\ \text{Acetic acid} \\ \text{Formic acid} \end{bmatrix} + CO_2 + H_2 \text{ (pH 4.0)}$$

Methyl red indicator turns red color

FIGURE 3 Glucose fermentation reaction with methyl red pH reagent

PART B: Methyl Red Test

PURPOSES

1. To determine the ability of microorganisms to oxidize glucose with the production and stabilization of high concentrations of acid end products.
2. To differentiate between all glucose-oxidizing enteric organisms, particularly *E. coli* and *E. aerogenes*.

PRINCIPLE

The hexose monosaccharide **glucose** is the major substrate oxidized by all enteric organisms for energy production. The end oducts of this process will vary depending the specific enzymatic pathways present in the bacteria. In this test the pH indicator methyl red detects the presence of large concentrations of acid end products. Although all enteric microorganisms ferment glucose with the production of organic acids, this test is of value in the separation of *E. coli* and *E. aerogenes*.

Both of these organisms initially produce organic acid end products during the early incubation period. The low acidic pH (4) is stabilized and maintained by *E. coli* at the end of incubation. During the later incubation period, *E. aerogenes* enzymatically converts these acids to nonacidic end products such as 2,3-butanediol and acetoin (acetylmethylcarbinol), resulting in an elevated pH of approximately 6. The glucose fermentation reaction generated by *E. coli* is illustrated in Figure 3.

As shown, the methyl red indicator in the pH range of 4 will turn red, which is indicative of a positive test. At a pH of 6, still indicating the presence of acid but with a lower hydrogen ion concentration, the indicator turns yellow and is a negative test. Produc-

tion and detection of the nonacidic end products from glucose fermentation by *E. aerogenes* is amplified in Part C of this exercise, the Voges-Proskauer test, which is performed simultaneously with the methyl red test.

MATERIALS

Cultures

24- to 48-hour trypticase soy broth cultures of *E. coli*, *E. aerogenes*, and *Klebsiella pneumoniae* for the short version. 24- to 48-hour trypticase soy broth cultures of the 13 previously listed organisms for the long version. Aliquots of these experimental cultures must be set aside from the Voges-Proskauer test.

Media

MR-VP broth per designated student group: four for the short version, 14 for the long version.

Reagent

Methyl red indicator.

Equipment

Bunsen burner, inoculating loop, test tubes, and glassware marking pencil.

PROCEDURE

1. Using sterile technique, inoculate each experimental organism into its appropriately labeled tube of medium by means of a loop inoculation. The last tube will serve as a control.
2. Incubate all cultures for 24 to 48 hours at 37°C.

IMViC Test

$$\text{Glucose} + O_2 \longrightarrow \underset{\text{acid}}{\text{Acetic}} \longrightarrow \begin{bmatrix} \text{2,3-butanediol} \\ \text{acetylmethylcarbinol} \end{bmatrix} + CO_2 + H_2 \text{ (ph 6.0)}$$

FIGURE 4   Glucose fermentation by *E. aerogenes*

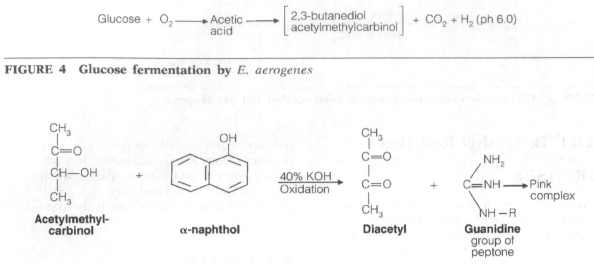

FIGURE 5   Acetylmethylcarbinol reaction with Barritt's reagent

PART C: Voges-Proskauer Test

PURPOSE

To differentiate further among enteric organisms such as *E. coli*, *E. aerogenes*, and *K. pneun   ?.*

PRINCIPLE

The Voges-Proskauer test determines the capability of some organisms to produce nonacidic or neutral end products, such as acetylmethylcarbinol, from the organic acids that result from glucose metabolism. This glucose fermentation, which is characteristic of *E. aerogenes*, is illustrated in Figure 4.

The reagent used in this test, Barritt's reagent, consists of a mixture of alcoholic α-naphthol and 40% potassium hydroxide solution. Detection of acetylmethylcarbinol requires this end product to be oxidized to a diacetyl compound. This reaction will occur in the presence of the α-naphthol catalyst and a guanidine group that is present in the peptone of the MR-VP medium. As a result, a pink complex is formed, imparting a rose color to the medium. The chemistry of this reaction is illustrated in Figure 5.

Development of a deep rose color in the culture 15 minutes following the addition of Barritt's reagent is indicative of the presence of acetylmethylcarbinol and represents a positive result. The absence of rose coloration is a negative result.

MATERIALS

Cultures

24- to 48-hour trypticase soy broth cultures of *E. coli*, *E. aerogenes*, and *K. pneumoniae* for the short version. 24- to 48-hour trypticase soy broth cultures of the 13 previously listed organisms for the long version. **Aliquots of these experimental cultures must be set aside from the methyl red test.**

Reagent

Barritt's reagents A and B.

Equipment

Bunsen burner, inoculating loop, and glassware marking pencil.

PROCEDURE

Refer to the methyl red test in Part B of this exercise.

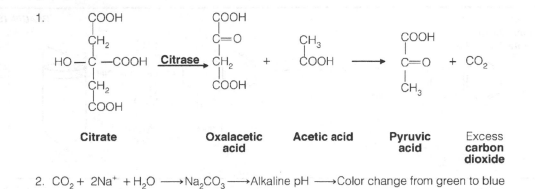

1.

| Citrate | Oxalacetic acid | Acetic acid | Pyruvic acid | Excess carbon dioxide |

2. $CO_2 + 2Na^+ + H_2O \longrightarrow Na_2CO_3 \longrightarrow$ Alkaline pH $\longrightarrow$ Color change from green to blue

FIGURE 6 Enzymatic degradation of citrate

PART D: Citrate Utilization Test

PURPOSE

To differentiate among enteric organisms on the basis of their ability to ferment citrate as a sole carbon source.

PRINCIPLE

In the absence of fermentable glucose or lactose, some microorganisms are capable of using **citrate** as a carbon source for their energy. This ability depends on the presence of a **citrate permease** that facilitates the transport of citrate in the cell. Citrate is the first major intermediate in the Krebs cycle and is produced by the condensation of active acetyl with oxalacetic acid. Citrate is acted on by the enzyme **citrase**, which produces oxalacetic acid and acetate. These products are then enzymatically converted to pyruvic acid and carbon dioxide. During this reaction the medium becomes alkaline—the carbon dioxide that is generated combines with sodium and water to form sodium carbonate, an alkaline product. The presence of sodium carbonate changes the bromthymol blue indicator incorporated into the medium from green to deep Prussian blue. This reaction is illustrated in Figure 6.

Following incubation, citrate-positive cultures are identified by the presence of growth on the surface of the slant, which is accompanied by blue coloration. Citrate-negative cultures will show no growth, and the medium will remain green.

MATERIALS

Cultures

24- to 48-hour trypticase soy broth cultures of *E. coli*, *E. aerogenes*, and *K. pneumoniae* for the short version. 24- to 48-hour trypticase soy broth cultures of the 13 previously listed organisms for the long version.

Media

Simmons citrate agar slants per designated student group: four for the short version, 14 for the long version.

Equipment

Bunsen burner, inoculating needle, test tube rack, and glassware marking pencil.

PROCEDURE

1. Using sterile technique, inoculate each organism into its appropriately labeled tube by means of a stab-and-streak inoculation. The last tube will serve as a control.
2. Incubate all cultures for 24 to 48 hours at 37°C.

IMViC Test

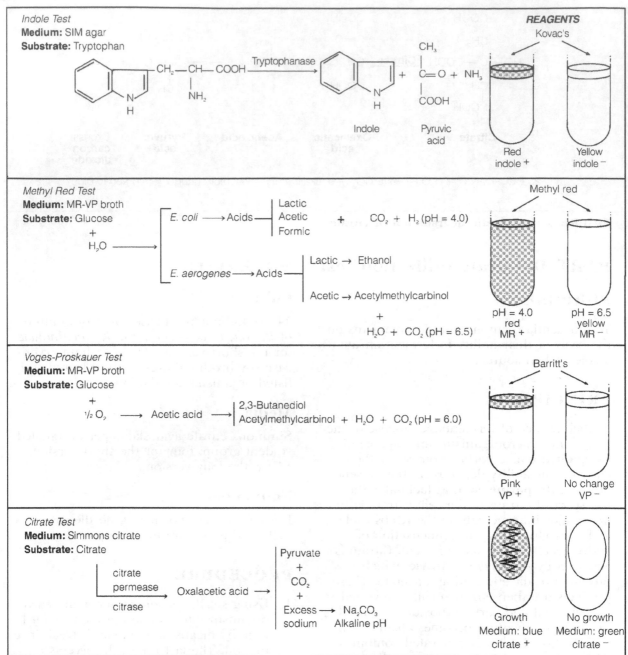

FIGURE 7   Summary of IMViC reactions

Name   Section   Date

OBSERVATIONS AND RESULTS

PART A: Indole Production Test

1. Add 10 drops of Kovac's reagent to all deep tube cultures and agitate the cultures gently.
2. Examine the color of the reagent layer in each culture. Record your results in the chart.
3. Based on your observations, determine and record whether or not each organism was capable of hydrolyzing the tryptophan.

✚ *Refer to the color-plate insert for illustration of these reactions.*

Bacterial Species	Color of Reagent Layer	Tryptophan Hydrolysis (+) or (−)
E. coli		
E. aerogenes		
K. pneumoniae		
S. dysenteriae		
S. typhimurium		
P. vulgaris		
' aeruginosa		
A. faecalis		
M. luteus		
S. lactis		
S. aureus		
B. cereus		
C. xerosis		
Control		

PART B: Methyl Red Test

1. Transfer approximately one-third of each culture into an empty test tube and set these tubes aside for the Voges-Proskauer test.
2. Add five drops of the methyl red indicator to the remaining aliquot of each culture.
3. Examine the color of all cultures. Record the results in the chart.
4. Based on your observations, determine and record whether or not each organism was capable of fermenting glucose with the production and maintenance of a high concentration of acid.

✚ *Refer to the color-plate insert for illustration of these reactions.*

PART C: Voges-Proskauer Test

1. To the aliquots of each broth culture separated during the methyl red test, add 10 drops of Barritt's reagent A and shake the cultures. Immediately add 10 drops of Barritt's reagent B and shake. Reshake the cultures every 3 to 4 minutes.

2. Examine and record the color of the cultures 15 minutes after the addition of Barritt's reagent.

3. Based on your observations, determine and record whether or not each organism was capable of fermenting glucose with ultimate production of acetylmethylcarbinol.

✚ *Refer to the color-plate insert for illustration of these reactions.*

	Methyl Red Test		Voges-Proskauer Test	
Bacterial Species	**Color of Medium**	**(+) or (−)**	**Color of Medium**	**(+) or (−)**
E. coli				
E. aerogenes				
K. pneumoniae				
S. dysenteriae				
S. typhimurium				
P. vulgaris				
P. aeruginosa				
A. faec.				
M. luteus				
S. lactis				
S. aureus				
B. cereus				
C. xerosis				
Control				

PART D: Citrate Utilization Test

1. Examine all agar slant cultures for the presence or absence of growth and coloration of the medium. Record your results in the chart.

2. Based on your observations, determine and record whether or not each organism was capable of using citrate as its sole source of carbon.

✚ *Refer to the color-plate insert for illustration of these reactions.*

Bacterial Species	Presence or Absence of Growth (+) or (−)	Color of Medium	Citrate Utilization (+) or (−)
E. coli			
E. aerogenes			
K. pneumoniae			
S. dysenteriae			
S. typhimurium			
P. vulgaris			
P. aeruginosa			
A. faecalis			
M. luteus			
S. lactis			
S. aureus			
B. cereus			
C. xerosis			
Control			

REVIEW QUESTIONS

Discuss the medical significance of the IMViC series of tests.

2. Explain the chemical mechanism for detecting indole in a bacterial culture.

3. Account for the development of alkalinity in cultures capable of using citrate as their sole carbon source.

IMViC Test

4. 🔍 In the carbohydrate fermentation test, we found that both *E. coli* and *E. aerogenes* produced the end products acid and gas. Account for the fact that *E. coli* is methyl red-positive and *E. aerogenes* is methyl red-negative.

5. 🔍 The end products of tryptophan degradation are indole and pyruvic acid. Why do we test for the presence of indole rather than pyruvic acid as the indicator of tryptophanase activity?

6. 🔍 Simmons citrate medium contains primarily inorganic ammonium, potassium, and sodium salts, plus organic citrate. What is the rationale for using a medium with this type of composition for the performance of the citrate utilization test?

27

Catalase Test

PURPOSE

To determine the ability of some microorganisms to degrade hydrogen peroxide by producing the enzyme catalase.

PRINCIPLE

During aerobic respiration, microorganisms produce hydrogen peroxide and, in some cases, an extremely toxic superoxide. Accumulation of these substances will result in death of the organism unless they can be enzymatically degraded. These substances are produced when aerobes, facultative anaerobes, and microaerophiles use the aerobic respiratory pathway, in which oxygen is the final electron acceptor, during degradation of rbohydrates for energy production. Organisms capable of producing **catalase** rapidly degrade hydrogen peroxide as illustrated:

$$2H_2O_2 \xrightarrow{\text{Catalase}} 2H_2O + O_2 \uparrow$$

Hydrogen peroxide   **Water**   **Free oxygen**

Aerobic organisms that lack catalase can degrade especially toxic superoxides using the enzyme **superoxide dismutase**; the end product of a superoxide dismutase is H_2O_2, but this is less toxic to the bacterial cells than are the superoxides.

The inability of strict anaerobes to synthesize catalase, peroxidase, or superoxide dismutase may explain why oxygen is poisonous to these microorganisms. In the absence of these enzymes, the toxic concentration of H_2O_2 cannot be degraded when these organisms are cultivated in the presence of oxygen.

Catalase production can be determined by adding the substrate H_2O_2 to an appropriately incubated trypticase soy agar slant culture. If catalase is present, the chemical reaction mentioned is indicated by bubbles of free oxygen gas ($O_2\uparrow$). This is a positive catalase test; the absence of bubble formation is a negative catalase test.

MATERIALS

Cultures

24- to 48-hour trypticase soy broth cultures of *Staphylococcus aureus*, *Micrococcus luteus*, and *Streptococcus lactis* for the short version. 24- to 48-hour trypticase soy broth cultures of the 13 previously listed organisms for the long version.

Media

Trypticase soy agar slants per designated student group: four for the short version, 14 for the long version.

Reagent

3% hydrogen peroxide.

Equipment

Bunsen burner, inoculating loop, test tube rack, and glassware marking pencil.

PROCEDURE

1. Using sterile technique, inoculate each experimental organism into its appropriately labeled tube by means of a streak inoculation. The last tube will serve as a control.
2. Incubate all cultures for 24 to 48 hours at 37°C.

Name	Section	Date

OBSERVATIONS AND RESULTS

1. Allow three or four drops of the 3% hydrogen peroxide to flow over the entire surface of each slant culture.
2. Examine each culture for the presence or absence of bubbling or foaming. Record your results in the chart.
3. Based on your observations, determine and record whether or not each organism was capable of catalase activity.

✚ *Refer to the color-plate insert for illustration of these reactions.*

Bacterial Species	Presence or Absence of Bubbling	Catalase Production (+) or (−)
E. coli		
E. aerogenes		
K. pneumoniae		
S. dysenteriae		
S. typhimurium		
P. vulgaris		
P. aeruginosa		
A. faecalis		
M. luteus		
S. lactis		
S. aureus		
B. cereus		
C. xerosis		
Control		

REVIEW QUESTIONS

1. Explain the toxic effect of O_2 on strict anaerobes.

2. Illustrate the chemical reaction involved in the degradation of hydrogen peroxide in the presence of catalase.

3. Would catalase be classified as an endoenzyme or an exoenzyme? Explain.

4. Account for the ability of streptococci to tolerate O_2 in the absence of catalase activity.

Use of Differential and Selective Media

PURPOSE

To become familiar with the use and function of specialized media for selection and differentiation of microorganisms.

PRINCIPLE

Numerous special-purpose media are available for functions such as:

1. Isolation of bacterial types from a mixed population of organisms.
2. Differentiation among closely related groups of bacteria on the basis of macroscopic appearance of the colonies and biochemical reactions within the medium.

   Enumeration of bacteria in sanitary microbiology, such as in water and sewage, and also in food and dairy products.
4. Assay of naturally occurring substances such as antibiotics, vitamins, and products of industrial fermentation.
5. Characterization and identification of bacteria by their abilities to produce chemical changes in different media.

In addition to nutrients necessary for the growth of all bacteria, special-purpose media contain one or more chemical compounds that are essential for their functional specificity. In this exercise, two types of media will be studied and evaluated.

Selective Media

These media are used to select (isolate) specific groups of bacteria. They incorporate chemical substances that inhibit the growth of one type of bacteria while permitting growth of another, thus facilitating bacterial isolation.

Differential Media

These can distinguish among morphologically and biochemically related groups of organisms. They incorporate chemical compounds that, following inoculation and incubation, produce a characteristic change in the appearance of bacterial growth and/or the medium surrounding the colonies, which permits differentiation.

The following media, which are representative of these two types, will be investigated in this exercise:

1. **Mannitol salt agar:** This medium contains a high salt concentration, 7.5% NaCl, which is inhibitory to the growth of most bacteria other than the staphylococci. The medium also performs a differential function: it contains the carbohydrate mannitol, which some staphylococci are capable of fermenting, and phenol red, a pH indicator for detecting acid produced by mannitol-fermenting staphylococci. These staphylococci exhibit a yellow zone surrounding their growth; staphylococci that do not ferment mannitol will not produce a change in coloration.

2. **Blood agar:** The blood that is incorporated into this medium is an enrichment ingredient for the cultivation of fastidious organisms such as the *Streptococcus* spp. The blood also permits demonstration of the hemolytic properties of some microorganisms, particularly the streptococci, whose hemolytic activities are classified as:

   a. **Gamma hemolysis:** No lysis of red blood cells results in no significant change in the appearance of the medium surrounding the colonies.

   b. **Alpha hemolysis:** Incomplete lysis of red blood cells, with reduction of hemoglobin to methemoglobin, results in a greenish halo around the bacterial growth.

   c. **Beta hemolysis:** Lysis of red blood cells with complete destruction and use of hemoglobin by the organism results in a clear zone surrounding the colonies. This hemolysis is produced by two types of beta hemolysins, namely **streptolysin O**, an antigenic, oxygen-labile enzyme, and **streptolysin S**, a nonantigenic, oxygen-stable lysin. The hemolytic reaction is enhanced when blood agar plates are streaked and simultaneously stabbed to show subsurface hemolysis by streptolysin O in an environment with reduced oxygen tension.

3. **MacConkey agar:** The inhibitory action of crystal violet on the growth of gram-positive organisms allows the isolation of gram-negative bacteria. Incorporation of the carbohydrate lactose, bile salts, and the pH indicator neutral red permits differentiation of enteric bacteria on the basis of their ability to ferment lactose. On this basis, enteric bacteria are separated into two groups:

   a. **Coliform bacilli** produce acid as a result of lactose fermentation. The bacteria exhibit a red coloration on their surface. *Escherichia coli* produce ter quantities of acid from lactose ᴛthan other coliform species. When this occurs, the medium surrounding the growth also becomes red because of the action of the acid that precipitates the bile salts, followed by absorption of the neutral red.

   b. **Dysentery, typhoid, and paratyphoid bacilli** are not lactose fermenters and therefore do not produce acid. The colonies appear uncolored and frequently transparent.

4. **Eosin-methylene blue agar (Levine):** Lactose and the dyes eosin and methylene blue permit differentiation between enteric lactose fermenters and nonfermenters as well as identification of the colon bacillus, *E. coli*. The *E. coli* colonies are blue-black with a metallic green sheen caused by the large quantity of acid that is produced and that precipitates the dyes onto the growth's surface. Other coliform bacteria, such as *Enterobacter aerogenes*, produce thick, mucoid, pink colonies on this medium. Enteric bacteria that do not ferment lactose produce colorless colonies, which, because of their transparency, appear to take on

the purple color of the medium. This medium is also partially inhibitory to the growth of gram-positive organisms, and thus gram-negative growth is more abundant.

5. **Phenylethyl alcohol agar:** This medium is used for the isolation of most gram-positive cocci. The phenylethyl alcohol is partially inhibitory to gram-negative organisms, which may form visible colonies whose size and number are much smaller than on other media.

MATERIALS

Cultures

24- to 48-hour trypticase soy broth cultures of *Enterobacter aerogenes*, *Escherichia coli*, *Streptococcus* var. Lancefield Group E, *Streptococcus mitis*, *Enterococcus faecalis*, *Staphylococcus aureus*, *Staphylococcus epidermidis*, and *Salmonella typhimurium*.

Media

Per designated student group: one each of mannitol salt agar plate, blood agar plate, MacConkey agar plate, eosin-methylene blue agar plate, and phenylethyl alcohol agar plate.

Equipment

Bunsen burner, inoculating loop, and glassware marking pencil.

PROCEDURE

1. Using the bacterial organisms listed in Step 2 below, prepare and inoculate each of the plates in the following manner:

   a. Appropriately label the cover of each plate as indicated in the section entitled "Laboratory Protocol."

   b. Divide each of the Petri dishes into the required number of sections (one section for each different organism) by marking the **bottom of the dish**. Label each section with the name of the organism to be inoculated as illustrated in Figure 1.

   c. Using sterile technique, inoculate all plates, except the blood agar plate, with the designated organisms by

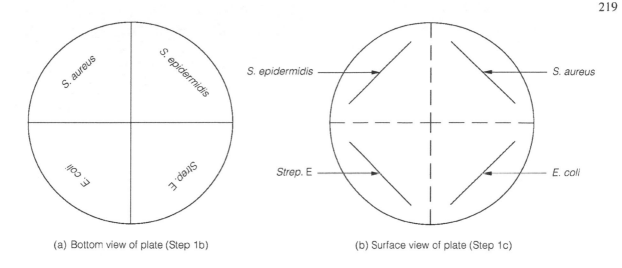

(a) Bottom view of plate (Step 1b) (b) Surface view of plate (Step 1c)

FIGURE 1   Mannitol salt agar plate preparation and inoculation procedure

making a single line of inoculation of each organism in its appropriate section. Be sure to close the Petri dish and flame the inoculating needle between inoculations of the different organisms. Refer to Figure 1 for an illustration of this procedure.

d. Using sterile technique, inoculate the blood agar plate as described in Step 1c. Upon completion of each single line of inoculation, use the inoculating loop and make three or four stabs at a 45° angle across the streak.

2. Inoculate each of the different media with the following:

a. Mannitol salt agar: *S. aureus, S. epidermidis, Streptococcus* var. Lancefield Group E, and *E. coli.*

b. Blood agar: *E. faecalis, S. mitis,* and *Streptococcus* var. Lancefield Group E.

c. MacConkey agar and eosin-methylene blue agar: *E. coli, E. aerogenes, S. typhimurium,* and *S. aureus.*

d. Phenylethyl alcohol agar: *E. coli, S. aureus,* and *E. faecalis.*

3. Incubate the phenylethyl alcohol agar plate in an inverted position for 48 to 72 hours at 37°C. Incubate the remaining plates in an inverted position for 24 to 48 hours at 37°C.

Name   Section   Date

OBSERVATIONS AND RESULTS

1. Carefully examine each of the plates. Note and record the following on the chart below:
   a. Amount of growth along line of inoculation as:
      0 = none; 1+ = scant; and 2+ = moderate to abundant.
   b. Appearance of the growth: coloration, transparency.
   c. Change in the appearance of the medium surrounding the growth: coloration, transparency indicative of hemolysis.

✚ *Refer to the color-plate insert for illustration of these reactions.*

Medium	Bacterial Species	Amount of Growth	Appearance of Growth	Appearance of Medium
Mannitol Salt Agar	E. coli			
	Streptococcus var. Lancefield Group E			
	S. aureus			
	S. epidermidis			
Blood Agar	S. mitis			
	E. faecalis			
	Streptococcus var. Lancefield Group E			
MacConkey Agar	E. coli			
	E. aerogenes			
	S. typhimurium			
	S. aureus			
Eosin–Methylene Blue Agar	E. coli			
	E. aerogenes			
	S. typhimurium			
	S. aureus			
Phenylethyl Alcohol Agar	E. coli			
	S. aureus			
	E. faecalis			

2. Indicate the specific selective and/or differential purpose of each of the following media:
   a. Mannitol salt agar:

   b. Blood agar:

c. MacConkey agar:

d. Eosin–methylene blue agar (Levine):

e. Phenylethyl alcohol agar:

REVIEW QUESTIONS

1. Explain the purpose of
   a. Crystal violet in the MacConkey agar medium:

   b. Blood in the blood agar medium:

   c. Eosin and methylene blue dyes in the eosin–methylene blue agar medium:

   d. High salt concentration in the mannitol salt agar medium:

   e. Lactose in the MacConkey agar medium:

   f. Phenylethyl alcohol in the phenylethyl alcohol agar medium:

2. A patient exhibits a boil on his neck. You, as a microbiology technician, are asked to identify and determine whether the causative organism is pathogenic. Describe the procedure that you would follow to make this determination.

Microbes Used in the Production of Foods

Objectives

After completing this exercise, you should be able to:

1. Explain how the activities of microorganisms are used to preserve food.
2. Define fermentation.
3. Produce an enjoyable product.

Background

Microbial fermentations are used to produce a wide variety of foods. **Fermentation** means different things to different people. In industrial usage, it is any large-scale microbial process occurring with or without air. To the biochemist, it is the group of metabolic processes that release energy from a sugar or other organic molecule, do not require oxygen or an electron transport system, and use an organic molecule as a final electron acceptor. In this exercise, we will examine a lactic acid fermentation used in the production of food.

In dairy fermentations, such as yogurt production, microorganisms use lactose and produce lactic acid without using oxygen. In nondairy fermentations, such as wine production, yeast use sucrose to produce ethyl alcohol and carbon dioxide under anaerobic conditions. If oxygen is available, the yeast will grow aerobically, liberating carbon dioxide and water as metabolic end-products.

Historically, milk has been fermented by selected microbes, with the resulting acidity preventing spoilage by acid-intolerant microbes. These "sour" milks have varied from country to country depending on the source of milk, conditions of culture, and microbial "starter" used. Milk from donkeys to zebras has been used, with the Russian *kumiss* (horse milk), containing 2% alcohol, and Swedish *surmjölk* (reindeer milk) being unusual examples. The bacteria yield lactic acid, and the yeast produce ethyl alcohol. Currently, two fermented cow milk products, buttermilk and yogurt, are widely used.

Buttermilk is the fluid left after cream is churned into butter. Today, buttermilk is actually prepared by souring true buttermilk or by adding bacteria to skim milk and then flavoring it with butterflake. *Lactococcus lactis* ferments the milk, producing lactic acid (sour);

and neutral fermentation products (diacetyls) are produced by *Leuconostoc.* Yogurt originated in the Balkan countries, goat milk being the primary source. Yogurt is milk that has been concentrated by heating and then fermented at elevated temperatures. *Streptococcus* produces lactic acid, and *Lactobacillus* produces the flavors and aroma of yogurt.

Materials

Homogenized milk

Nonfat dry milk

Large beaker

Stirring rod

Thermometer

Glass test tube

Hot plate or ring stand and asbestos pad

5 ml pipette

Styrofoam or paper cups with lids

Second period:

Plastic spoons

Petri plate containing trypticase soy agar

pH paper

Gram stain reagents

Optional: jam, jelly, honey, and so on

Culture

Commercial yogurt or *Streptococcus thermophilus* and *Lactobacillus bulgaricus*

Techniques Required

Gram staining

Plate streaking

Pipetting

Procedure

Be sure all glassware is clean.

1. Add 100 ml of milk per person (in your group) to a wet beaker (wash out the beaker first with water to decrease the sticking of the milk). Put a thermometer in a glass test tube containing water before placing it in the beaker.
2. Heat the milk on a hot plate or over a burner on an asbestos pad placed on a ring stand, to about 80°C for 10 to 20 minutes. Stir occasionally. Do not let it boil. Why is the milk heated? _____

   _____
3. Cool the milk to about 65°C and add 3 g of non-fat dry milk per person. Stir to dissolve. Why is dry milk added? _____

   _____
4. Rapidly cool the milk to about 45°C. Pour the milk equally into the cups.
5. Inoculate each cup with 1 to 2 teaspoonfuls of commercial yogurt, or 2.5 ml *S. thermophilus* and 2.5 ml *L. bulgaricus*. Cover and label the cups.

6. Incubate the cups at 45°C for 4 to 18 hours or until they are firm (custardlike).
7. Cool the yogurt to about 5°C. Save a small amount for steps 8 through 10. Then taste it with a clean spoon. Add jam or some other flavor if you desire. Eat!
8. Determine the pH of the yogurt.

> **Do not work with other bacteria or perform other exercises while eating the yogurt.**

9. Make a smear, and after heat-fixing it, Gram stain it. Record your results.
10. Streak for isolation on trypticase soy agar. Incubate the plate, inverted, at 45°C.
11. After distinct colonies are visible, record your observations. Prepare Gram stains from each different colony.

Microbes Used in the Production of Foods

LABORATORY REPORT

Name _____

Date _____

Lab Section _____

Purpose _____

_____

_____

Observations

Yogurt characteristics:

Taste: _____

Consistency: _____

Odor: _____

pH: _____

Gram stain results: _____

_____

Streak plate results: _____

_____

_____

Gram stain of isolated colonies: _____

_____

Questions

1. How can pathogens enter yogurt, and how can this be prevented? _____

_____

_____

2. What could cause an inferior product in a microbial fermentation process? _____

_____

3. How are microbial fermentations used to preserve foods? _____

_____

4. When the yogurt is Gram stained, what result would indicate that the yogurt is contaminated? _____

_____

Critical Thinking

1. What was the source of the bacteria and yeast originally used in dairy product fermentations and breads?

2. Describe how you would show that *Streptococcus* and *Lactobacillus* are in commercial yogurt.

3. How would consumption of yogurt on a regular basis affect the indigenous microbiota of the intestinal tract?

29

Wine Production

PURPOSE

To become acquainted with wine production by the fermentative activities of yeast cells.

PRINCIPLE

Wine is a product of the natural fermentation of the juices of grapes and other fruits, such as peaches, pears, plums, and apples, by the action of yeast cells. This biochemical conversion of juice to wine occurs when the yeast cells enzymatically degrade the fruit sugars fructose and glucose first to acetaldehyde and then to alcohol, as illustrated in Figure 1.

Grapes containing 20% to 30% sugar concentration will yield wines with an

:ohol content of approximately 10% to
ı ͻ%. Also present in grapes are acids and minerals whose concentrations are increased in the finished product and that are responsible for the characteristic tastes and bouquets of different wines. For red wine, the crushed grapes must be fermented with their skins to allow extraction of their color into the juice. White wine is produced from the juice of white grapes.

The commercial production of wine is a long and exacting process. First, the grapes are crushed or pressed to express the juice, which is called **must**. Potassium metabisulfite is added to the must to retard the growth of acetic acid bacteria, molds, and wild yeast that are endogenous to grapes in the vineyard. A wine-producing strain of yeast, *Saccharomyces cerevisiae* var. *ellipsoideus*, is used to inoculate the must, which is then incubated for 3 to 5 days under aerobic conditions at 21°C to 32°C. This is followed by an anaerobic incubation period. The wine is then aged for a period of 1 to 5 years in aging tanks or wooden barrels. During this time, the wine is clarified of any turbidity, thereby producing volatile esters that are responsible for characteristic flavors. The clarified product is then filtered, pasteurized at 60°C for 30 minutes, and bottled.

This experiment is a modified method in which white wine is produced from white grape juice. You will examine the fermenting wine at 1-week intervals during the incubation period for:

1. Total acidity (expressed as % tartaric acid): To a 10-ml aliquot of the fermenting wine, add 10 ml of distilled water and 5 drops of 1% phenolphthalein solution. Mix and titrate to the first persistent pink color with 0.1N sodium hydroxide.

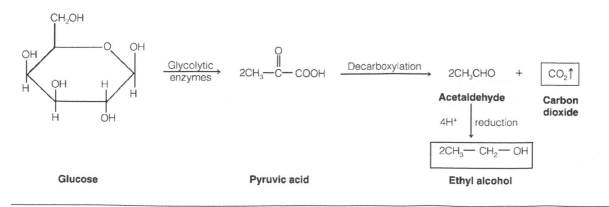

FIGURE 1   Biochemical pathway for alcohol production

Calculate total acidity using the following formula:

$$\% \text{ tartaric acid} = \frac{\text{ml alkali} \times \text{normality of alkali} \times 7.5}{\text{weight of sample in gm}^*}$$

*1 ml = 1 gm.

2. Volatile acidity (expressed as % acetic acid): Following titration, calculate volatile acidity using the following formula:

$$\% \text{ acetic acid} = \frac{\text{ml alkali} \times \text{normality of alkali} \times 6.0}{\text{weight of sample in gm}^*}$$

*1 ml = 1 gm.

3. Alcohol (expressed as volume %): Optional; can be determined by means of an ebulliometer.

4. Aroma: Fruity, yeastlike, sweet, none.

5. Clarity: Clear, turbid.

MATERIALS

Cultures

50 ml of white grape juice broth culture of *Saccharomyces cerevisiae* var. *ellipsoideus* incub. ' 'or 48 hours at 25°C.

Media

Per designated student group: 500 ml of pasteurized Welch's® commercial white grape juice.

Reagents

1% phenolphthalein solution, 0.1N sodium hydroxide, and sucrose.

Equipment

1-liter Erlenmeyer flask, one-holed rubber stopper containing a 2-inch glass tube plugged with cotton, pan balance, spatula, glassine paper, 10-ml graduated cylinder, ebulliometer (optional), and burette or pipette for titration.

PROCEDURE

1. Pour 500 ml of the white grape juice into the 1-liter Erlenmeyer flask. Add 20 gm of sucrose and the 50 ml of S. *cerevisiae* grape juice broth culture (10% starter culture). Close the flask with the stopper containing a cotton plugged air vent.

2. After 2 days and 4 days of incubation, add 20 gm of sucrose to the fermenting wine.

3. Incubate the fermenting wine for 21 days at 25°C.

Name   Section   Date

OBSERVATIONS AND RESULTS

1. Using uninoculated white grape juice:
   a. Perform a titration to determine total acidity and volatile acidity.
   b. Note aroma and clarity.
   c. Determine volume % alcohol (optional).
2. Record your results in the chart.
3. At 7-day intervals, using samples of the fermenting wine, repeat Steps 1a though 1c and record your results in the chart.

	Grape Juice	Fermenting Wine		
		7 days	14 days	21 days
% Tartaric acid				
% Acetic acid				
Volume % alcohol				
Aroma				
Clarity				

REVIEW QUESTIONS

1. What is the purpose of adding sulfite to the must?

2. Explain what occurs during the aging process in the commercial preparation of wine.

230

3. What are the chemical end products of fermentation?

4. How are white and red wines produced?

5. Why is wine pasteurized? Would it be preferable to sterilize the wine? Explain.

30

PHYSIOLOGICAL UNKNOWN TEST
(Second Unknown Bacterial Identification Test)

OBJECTIVES

1. To apply skills learned throughout the course for determinative bacteriology.
2. Use morphological, physiological, biochemical tests, and stain reactions to identify bacterial cultures.
3. Determine the names of bacteria by *Genus & species* with the help of flow charts.
4. Report results and submit for grading.

PRNCIPLE

Now that you are at the end of this course, you should be competent in microbiological techniques. This Exercise gives you opportunity to demonstrate your skills by identifying unknown bacterial cultures in greater details than in the first Unknown Test. Two slant cultures of unknown bacteria, identified only by numbers and letters, will be given to you for this Exercise. Using a combination of distinguishing characteristics and a flow chart, you will determine the actual names of the bacteria in the unknown cultures! Several tests will require inoculation and incubation. Therefore, this Exercise is scheduled for two weeks. In the second week, you will complete physiological tests that require incubation.

MATERIALS

     Pure cultures of unidentified bacteria on slants with a number, labeled "A" and "B".
2. Ixnoculating loop, glass slides, and cover glasses.
3. Compound light microscopes, staining rack, and bottles of staining reagents.
4. Culture media for selected Physiological and Biochemical Tests.
5. Flow charts derived from *Bergey's Manual of Systematic Bacteriology*.

PROCEDURE – WEEK 1

1. Personalize a copy of the Second Unknown Report sheet by writing -
    a.   Your Specimen number, Name, Table number, Seat number, and Lab Day.
2. Prepare a backup of each specimen by making a sub-culture.
3. Refer to your notes or Manual and perform physiological tests on specimens A and B.
4. Perform morphological tests, prepare slides, and stain specimens.
5. Use the oil immersion objective lens to observe each slide.
6. Record your observations for each Specimen -
    a.   Draw **one** cell to represent the typical shape of each specimen;
    b.   Draw between 4 and 8 cells to show how the cells are arranged;
    c.   Use (+) or (-) signs only to record Gram, Acidfast, and Endospore stain results.

7. Save all slides and incubate inoculated media and subcultures until the next lab.

PROCEDURE – WEEK 2

1. Complete any morphological tests and physiological or biochemical tests after incubation.
2. Use (+) or (-) signs only to record and interpret all completed results with flow chart.
3. Identify unknown specimens "A" and "B" and write the names you arrived at.
4. Hand completed report sheet to your instructor for grading. Keep a copy for your records.
5. Discard all bacterial cultures, including subcultures and incubated samples.

Second Bacterial Identification Report Sheet
(Second Unknown Test)

LAST NAME_____ FIRST NAME_____

DATE _____ TABLE No. _____ SEAT No. _____

LAB DAY/TIME _____

SPECIMEN No. _____	UNKNOWN CULTURE 'A'	UNKNOWN CULTURE 'B'

M O R P H O L O G I C A L   T E S T S

SHAPE		
ARRANGEMENT		
GRAM STAIN		
:IDFAST		
ENDOSPORE		

C A R B O H Y D R A T E   F E R M E N T A T I O N S

LACTOSE	[Acid]	[Gas]	[Acid]	[Gas]
DEXTROSE	[Acid]	[Gas]	[Acid]	[Gas]
MANNITOL	[Acid]	[Gas]	[Acid]	[Gas]

P H Y S I O L O G I C A L   T E S T S

NITRATE REDUCTION		
CITRATE UTILIZATION		
STARCH HYDROLYSIS		
CATALASE TEST		
METHYL RED TEST		
NAME OF BACTERIUM		

Flow Chart for Identifying Gram Positive Bacteria

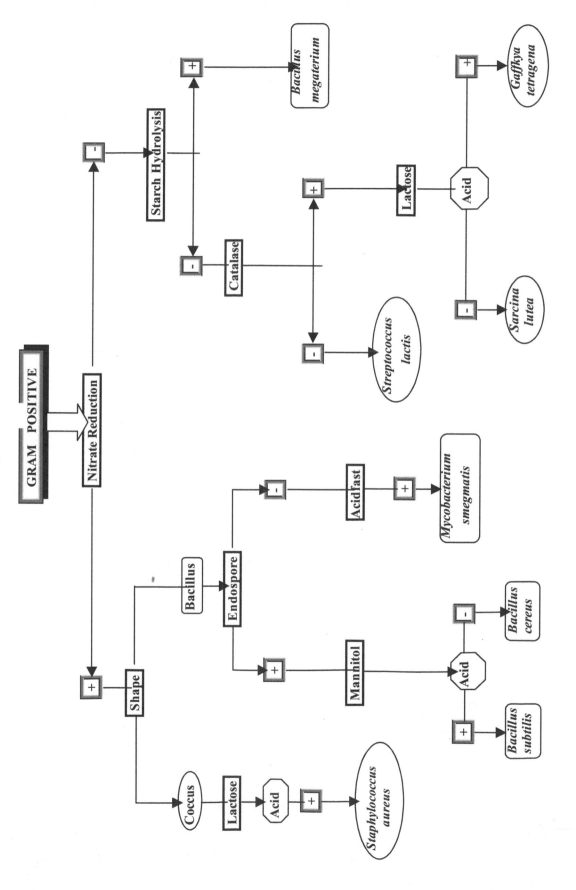

236

237

Flow Chart for Identifying Gram Negative Bacteria

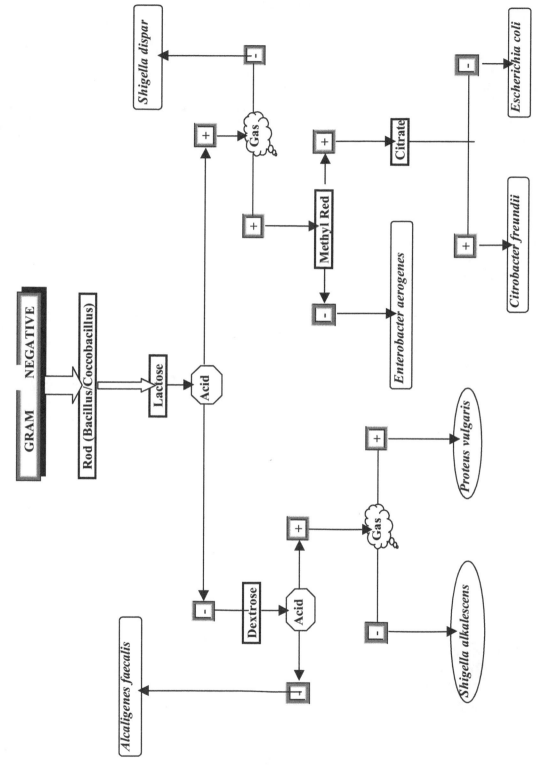

238

Rapid Identification Methods

Objectives

After completing this exercise, you should be able to:

1. Evaluate three methods of identifying enterics.
2. Name three advantages of the "systems approach" over conventional tube methods.

Background

The clinical microbiology laboratory must identify bacteria quickly and accurately. Accuracy is improved by using a series of standardized tests. The IMViC tests were developed as a means of separating members of the Enterobacteriaceae (enterics), particularly the coliforms,* using a standard combination of four tests. Each capital letter in **IMViC** represents a test; the *i* is added for easier pronunciation. The tests are as follows:

I for indole production from tryptophan

M for methyl red test for acid production from glucose

V for the Voges–Proskauer test for production of acetoin from glucose

C for the use of citrate as the sole carbon source. The Simmons citrate agar used in this exercise contains the indicator bromthymol blue. Citric acid will be the only source of carbon; therefore, only organisms capable of using citric acid as a source of carbon will grow. When the citric acid is metabolized, an excess of sodium and ammonium ions results, and the indicator turns from green to blue, indicating alkaline conditions. (See color plate III.10.)

Although variation among strains does exist, IMViC reactions for selected species of the Enterobacteriaceae are given in Table 1.

Rapid identification methods have been developed which provide a large number of results from one inoculation. Examples are Enterotube® II** and API 20E®*** for identifying oxidase-negative, gram-negative bacteria belonging to the family Enterobacteriaceae.

*Enterobacteriaceae are aerobic or facultatively anaerobic, gram-negative, nonendospore-forming, rod-shaped bacteria. Coliforms are Enterobacteriaceae that ferment lactose with acid and gas formation within 48 hours at 35°C.
**BD Bioscience, Cockeysville, MD 21030.
***bioMérieux Vitek, Inc., Hazelwood, MO 63042.

Table 1
IMViC Reactions for Selected Species of the Enterobacteriaceae

Species	Indole	Methyl Red	Voges–Proskauer	Citrate
Escherichia coli	+(v)	+	–	–
Citrobacter freundii	–	+	–	+
Enterobacter aerogenes	–	–	+	+
Enterobacter cloacae	–	–	+	+
Serratia marcescens	–	+ or –*	+	+
Proteus vulgaris	+	+	–	–(v)
Proteus mirabilis	–	+	–or +**	+(v)

v = variable
*Majority of strains give + results
**Majority of strains give results

Enterotube® II (see color plate III.7) is divided into twelve compartments, each containing a different substrate in agar. API 20E® (see color plate III.5) consists of twenty microtubes containing dehydrated substrates. The substrates are rehydrated by adding a bacterial suspension. No culturing beyond the initial isolation is necessary with these systems. Comparisons between these rapid identification methods and conventional culture methods show that they are as accurate as conventional test tube methods.

Computerized analysis of test results increases accuracy because each test is given a point value. Tests that are more important than others get more points. The IMViC tests are four tests of equal value.

As commercial identification systems are developed, they can provide greater standardization in identification because they overcome the limitations of hunting through a key, differences in media preparation, and evaluation of tests within a laboratory or between different laboratories. They also save time, money, and labor.

Materials

Petri plate containing nutrient agar

IMViC tests and reagents

Enterotube® II and reagents

API 20E® tray and reagents

Tube containing 5.0 ml sterile saline

5 ml pipette

Oxidase reagent

Mineral oil

Sterile Pasteur pipette

Culture

Unknown enteric # _____

Techniques Required

Inoculating loop and needle

Aseptic technique

MRVP tests

Fermentation tests

Protein catabolism

Respir

Procedure

Isolation

1. Streak the nutrient agar plate with your unknown for isolation and to determine purity of the culture. Incubate the plate, inverted, at 35°C for 24 to 48 hours. Record the appearance of the colonies.
2. Determine the oxidase reaction of one of the colonies remaining on the plate. Why? _____

   How will you determine the oxidase reaction? ___
   _____
   _____

IMViC Tests

1. Inoculate tubes of tryptone broth (indole test), MRVP broths, and Simmons citrate agar with your unknown.
2. Incubate the tubes at 35°C for 48 hours or longer; perform the appropriate tests, and record your results.

Enterotubet II (Figure 1)

1. Remove both caps from the Enterotube® II. One end of the wire is straight and is used to pick up the inoculum; the bent end of the wire is the

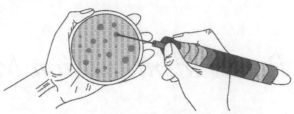

(a) Pick a well-isolated colony with the inoculating end of the wire.

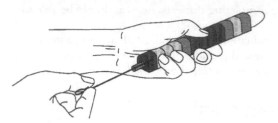

(b) Hold the bent end of the wire and withdraw the needle through all twelve compartments with a turning motion.

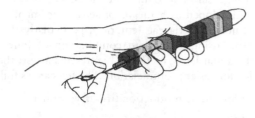

(c) Reinsert the wire through all twelve compartments. Then withdraw to the notch on the wire. Break the wire at the notch.

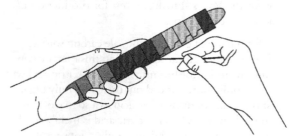

(d) Using the broken wire, punch holes through the foil covering the air inlets in the last eight compartments. Replace the caps loosely.

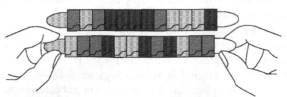

(e) After incubation, compare the tube to an uninoculated one to record results.

Figure 1

Inoculating an Enterotube® II.

Table 2

Enterotube® II Biochemical Reactions

Test	Comments	Indicator Changed	
		From	To
GLU	Acid from glucose	Red	Yellow
GAS	Gas produced from fermentation of glucose trapped in this compartment, causing separation of the wax		
LYS	Lysine decarboxylase	Yellow	Purple
ORN	Ornithine decarboxylase	Yellow	Purple
H_2S	Ferrous ion reacts with sulfide ions, forming a black precipitate		
IND	Kovacs reagent is added to the H_2S/IND compartment to detect indole	Beige	Red
ADON	Adonitol fermentation	Red	Yellow
LAC	Lactose fermentation	Red	Yellow
ARAB	Arabinose fermentation	Red	Yellow
SORB	Sorbitol fermentation	Red	Yellow
V–P	Voges–Proskauer reagents detect acetoin	Beige	Red
DUL	Dulcitol fermentation	Green	Yellow
PA	Phenylpyruvic acid released from phenylalanine after its deamination combines with iron salts to form a black precipitate		
UREA	Ammonia changes the pH of the medium	Yellow	Pink
CIT	Citric acid used as a carbon source	Green	Blue

Source: BD Bioscience, Cockeysville, MD 21030.

handle. Holding the Enterotube® II, pick a well-isolated colony with the inoculating end of the wire (Figure 1a). Avoid touching the agar with the needle.

2. Inoculate the Enterotube® II by holding the bent end of the wire and twisting; the tip of the wire should be visible in the citrate compartment. Withdraw the needle through all twelve compartments using a turning motion (Figure 1b).

3. Reinsert the needle into the Enterotube® II, using a turning motion, through all twelve compartments until the notch on the wire is aligned with the opening of the tube. Break the wire at the notch by bending it (Figure 1c). The portion of the needle remaining in the tube maintains anaerobic conditions necessary for fermentation, production of gas, and decarboxylation.

4. Punch holes with the broken-off wire through the foil covering the air inlets of the last eight compartments (adonitol through citrate) to provide aerobic conditions (Figure 1d). Replace the caps on both ends of the tube.

Discard the handle in disinfectant.

5. Incubate the tube lying on its flat surface at 35°C for 24 hours.

6. Interpret and record all reactions (see Table 2) in the Laboratory Report. Read all the other tests *before* the indole and V–P tests, which follow.

   a. Indole test. Place the Enterotube® II horizontally and melt a small hole in the plastic film covering the H_2S/indole compartment using a warm inoculating loop. Add 1 to 2 drops of Kovacs reagent, and allow the reagent to contact the agar surface. A positive test is indicated by a red color within 10 seconds.

b. V–P test. Add 2 drops of 20% KOH containing 5% α-naphthol to the V–P compartment. A positive test is indicated by development of a red color within 20 minutes.

7. Indicate each positive reaction by circling the number appearing below the appropriate compartment of the Enterotube® II outlined in the Laboratory Report. Add the circled numbers only within each bracketed section, and enter this sum in the space provided below the arrow. Note that the V–P test is used as a confirming test only. Read the five numbers in these spaces across as a five-digit number in the *Computer Coding and Identification System.**

8. Dispose of the Enterotube® II by placing it in the autoclave bag.

API 20Et (Figure 2)

1. Prepare a bacterial suspension by touching the center of a well-isolated colony with a sterile loop, and thoroughly mix the inoculum in 5 ml of sterile saline (Figure 2a).

2. Place 5 ml of tap water into the corrugated incubation tray, to provide a humid atmosphere during incubation.

3. U~:~~ ~ sterile Pasteur pipette, tilt the API 20E® tr   . fill the tube section of the microtubes with the bacterial suspension. Fill the tube *and* cupule sections of the CIT, VP, and GEL tubes (Figure 2b).

4. After inoculation, completely fill the cupule section of the ADH, LDC, ODC, H_2S, and URE tubes with mineral oil to create anaerobic conditions (Figure 2c).

5. Place the plastic lid on the tray and incubate the strip for 24 hours at 35°C (Figure 2d). If the strip

cannot be read after 24 hours, remove the strip from the incubator and refrigerate it.

6. Interpret and record all reactions (see Table 3) in the Laboratory Report. Read all the other tests before the TDA, VP, and IND, which follow.
   a. TDA test. Add 1 drop 10% ferric chloride. A positive test is brownish-red. Indole-positive organisms may produce an orange color; this is a negative TDA reaction.
   b. V–P test. Add 1 drop of V–P reagent II (KOH), then 1 drop of V–P reagent I (α-napthol). A positive reaction produces a red color (not pale pink) after 10 minutes.
   c. Indole test. Add 1 drop of Kovacs reagent. A red ring after 2 minutes indicates a positive reaction.
   d. Nitrate reduction. Before adding reagents, look for bubbles in the GLU tube. Bubbles indicate reduction of nitrate to N_2. Add 2 drops of nitrate reagent A (dimethyl-α-napthylamine) and 2 drops of nitrate reagent B (sulfanilic acid). A positive reaction (red) may take 2 to 3 minutes to develop. A negative test can be confirmed by adding zinc dust.

7. Indicate each positive reaction with a (+) in the appropriate compartment of the Laboratory Report. Add the points for each positive reaction within each bold-outlined section. Read the seven numbers across as a seven-digit number in the *API 20E Analytical Profile Index** or use the automated Voice Response System.*** Nitrate reduction is a confirming test and not part of the seven-digit code.

8. Dispose of the API strip, tray, and lid by placing them in the autoclave bag.

---

*BD Bioscience, Cockeysville, MD 21030.

**bioMérieux Vitek, Inc., Hazelwood, MO 63042.
***The Voice Response System is available at 1-800-645-7056.

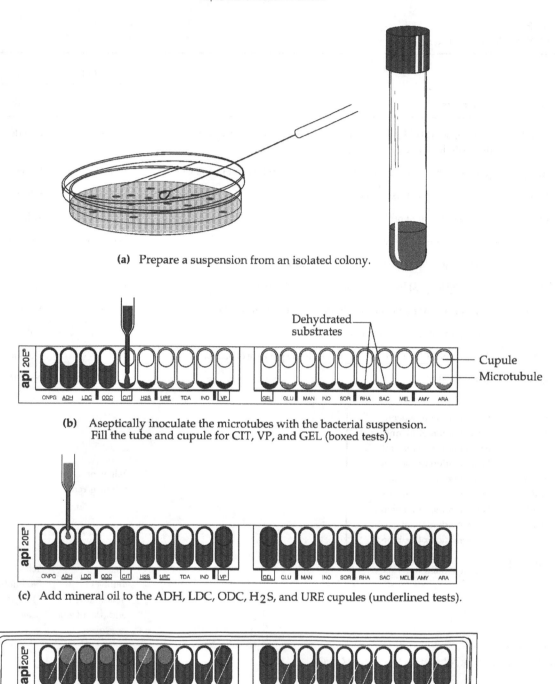

(a) Prepare a suspension from an isolated colony.

(b) Aseptically inoculate the microtubes with the bacterial suspension. Fill the tube and cupule for CIT, VP, and GEL (boxed tests).

(c) Add mineral oil to the ADH, LDC, ODC, H_2S, and URE cupules (underlined tests).

(d) Incubate the strip in its plastic tray.

Figure 2
Inoculating the API 20E® system.

Table 3
API 20E® Biochemical Reactions

Test	Comments	Indicator	
		Positive	Negative
ONPG	O-nitrophenyl-β-D-galactopyranoside is hydrolyzed by the enzyme that hydrolyzes lactose	Yellow	Colorless
ADH	Arginine dihydrolase transforms arginine into ornithine, NH_3, and CO_2	Red	Yellow
LDC	Decarboxylation of lysine liberates cadaverine	Red	Yellow
ODC	Decarboxylation of ornithine produces putrescine	Red	Yellow
CIT	Citric acid used as sole carbon source	Dark blue	Light green
H_2S	Blackening indicates reduction of thiosulfate to H_2S	Black	No blackening
URE	Urea is hydrolyzed by the enzyme urease to NH_3 and CO_2	Red	Yellow
TDA	Deamination of tryptophan produces indole and pyruvic acid	Brown	Yellow
IND	Kovacs reagent is added to detect indole	Red ring	Yellow
VP	Addition of KOH and α-naphthol detects the presence of acetoin	Red	Colorless
GEL	Gelatin hydrolysis	Diffusion of pigment	No diffusion
GLU	Fermentation of glucose		
MA	Fermentation of mannitol		
INO	Fermentation of inositol		
SOR	Fermentation of sorbitol		
RHA	Fermentation of rhamnose	Yellow or yellow-green	Blue or green
SAC	Fermentation of sucrose		
MEL	Fermentation of melibiose		
AMY	Fermentation of amygdalin		
ARA	Fermentation of arabinose		
NO_2 / N_2 gas	Nitrate reduction	Red / Bubbles / Yellow after addition of zinc	Yellow / No bubbles / Orange after reagents and zinc

Source: bioMérieux Vitek Inc., Hazelwood, MO 63042.

Rapid Identification Methods

Purpose _____

_____

_____

Data

Unknown # _____

Appearance on nutrient agar: _____

Oxidase reaction: _____

IViC

Indicate positive (+) and negative (−) results for each test.

Indole: _____

Methyl red: _____

V–P: _____

Citrate: _____

Enterotube® II

Circle the number corresponding to each positive reaction below the appropriate compartment. Then determine the five-digit code.

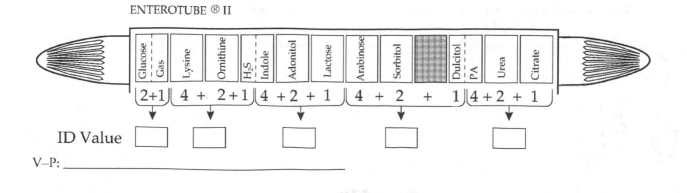

ENTEROTUBE ® II

ID Value

V–P: _____

API 20E®

Indicate positive (+) and negative (–) results in the Results line. Then determine the seven-digit code.

	ONPG 1	ADH 2	LDC 4	ODC 1	CIT 2	H₂S 4	URE 1	TDA 2	IND 4	VP 1	GEL 2	GLU 4
Results												
Profile number												

	MAN 1	INO 2	SOR 4	RHA 1	SAC 2	MEL 4	AMY 1	ARA 2	Oxidase 4	NO₂	N₂ GAS
Results											
Profile number											

Questions

1. What species was identified in unknown # _____ by the IMViC tests? _____

By the API 20E®? _____

By the Enterotube® II? _____

2. Di᷄   ree methods agree? _____ If not, explain any discrepancies. _____

_____

_____

3. Which method did you prefer? _____ Why? _____

_____

_____

4. Why are systems developed to identify Enterobacteriaceae? _____

_____

_____

5. Why is an oxidase test performed on a culture before using API 20E® and Enterotube® II to identify the culture?

_____

_____

Critical Thinking

1. Why should the first digit in the five-digit Enterotube® II ID value be equal to or greater than 2, and the fourth digit in the API 20E® profile number be equal to or greater than 4?

2. Why can one species have two or more numbers in a rapid identification system? (For example, *E. coli* is Enterotube® II numbers 34540 and 34560; *Citrobacter braakii* is API 20E® numbers 3504552 and 3504553.)

3. Use Table 1 to give an example of a limitation of the IMViC tests.

Sauerkraut Production

PURPOSE

To become acquainted with the microbiological production of sauerkraut.

PRINCIPLE

Sauerkraut is a classic example of a food of plant origin produced by microbial fermentation. Its preparation requires the fermentative activities of a mixed microbial flora, including *Leuconostoc mesenteroides*, *Lactobacillus plantarum*, *Lactobacillus brevis*, and *Enterococcus faecalis*.

In the production of sauerkraut, shredded cabbage is treated with sodium chloride, which creates an osmotic environment in which plasmolysis occurs, thereby extracting e juice from the cabbage tissue. The resultant brine solution favors the growth of lactic acid–producing microorganisms and inhibits the growth of other microorganisms. The lactic acid is responsible for the characteristic kraut flavor and also acts as a preservative by inhibiting the growth of microorganisms that cause food spoilage.

Production of the lactic acid is initiated by *L. mesenteroides*, which are cocci, and sustained by *L. plantarum*, which are bacilli. When the acid concentration reaches a level of 0.7% to 1%, the fermentative activities of *L. mesenteroides* cease and the final stages of the process are carried out by *L. plantarum*, *L. brevis*, and *E. faecalis*. The finished product contains a total acidity of 1.5% to 2%, of which lactic acid represents 1% to 1.5%.

In this experiment, you will prepare two samples of sauerkraut, one for sampling and testing of the final product and the other for testing at specific intervals during incubation for:

1. Odor: Acid, earthy, spicy, or putrid.
2. Color: Brown, pink, straw yellow, pale yellow, or colorless.
3. Texture:
   a. Soft: Fermentation initiated by *L. plantarum* rather than *L. mesenteroides*.
   b. Slimy: Rapid growth of *Lactobacillus cucumeris* at elevated temperatures.
   c. Rotted: Spoilage by bacteria, yeast, or molds.
4. pH: The pH of the finished product should be in the range of 3.1 to 3.7.
5. Total acidity expressed as % lactic acid:
   a. Place 10 ml of the fermentation juice and 10 ml distilled water into an Erlenmeyer flask. Boil to drive off the CO_2.
   b. Cool and add 5 drops of 1% phenolphthalein to the diluted juice.
   c. Titrate to the first persistent sample with pink color with 0.1N NaOH.
   d. Calculate % lactic acid as follows:

$$\% \text{ lactic acid} = \frac{\text{ml of alkali} \times \text{normality of alkali} \times 9}{\text{weight of sample in gm*}}$$

   *1 ml = 1 gm.

6. Microscopic appearance of the microbial flora.

MATERIALS

Media

Per designated student group: two heads of cabbage.

Reagents

1% phenolphthalein, 0.1N NaOH, methylene blue, and uniodized table salt.

Equipment

Two wide-mouthed jars with covers, two wooden boards to fit into jars, two heavy weights, cheesecloth, pH meter or indicator paper, pan balance, microscope, Bunsen burner, inoculating loop, glass slides, cover-slips, 10-ml disposable pipettes, mechanical pipetting device, knife, and Erlen-meyer flask.

PROCEDURE

1. Remove the outer leaves and all bruised tissues from each of the cabbage heads.
2. Halve, core, and wash the heads in tap water.
3. Shred the cabbage.
4. Weigh the shredded cabbage on a pan balance and separate into two equal portions.
5. Weigh out the table salt in amounts equal to 3% of the weight of each of the portions of shredded cabbage.
6. Place the shredded cabbage and salt in alternating layers in the two wide-mouthed jars.
7. Place a wooden board over each of the mixtures and press gently to squeeze out a layer of juice from the cabbage.
8. Place a weight on each of the boards and cover the jars with cheesecloth.
9. Incubate the jars for 14 days at 30°C.

Name   Section   Date

OBSERVATIONS AND RESULTS

Examine the sauerkraut preparation on Days 2, 7, 14, and 21 of incubation as follows:

1. Examine the fermenting cabbage for aroma, texture, and color. Record your results in the chart.
2. With a 10-ml pipette, remove 10 ml of the fermentation juice.
    a. Using methylene blue, prepare a stained slide preparation for microscopic examination.
    b. Using the pH meter or indicator paper, determine the pH of the juice.
    c. Perform a titration of the juice to determine the % lactic acid present.

    Record your results in the chart.

Result	Sauerkraut Preparation			
	2 days	7 days	14 days	21 days
Odor				
Color				
Texture				
% Lactic acid				
H				
Draw microbial flora if present.	◯	◯	◯	◯

3. Based on your observations, was there any indication of microbial spoilage of your sauerkraut? Explain.

REVIEW QUESTIONS

1. Discuss the importance of the specific sequential activity of the microbial flora responsible for sauerkraut production.

Sauerkraut Production

252

2. What is the function of the salt used in preparing sauerkraut?

3. Why is uniodized salt used in this procedure?

4. Explain the production of slimy or rotten kraut.

5. How does the process of fermentation aid in food preservation?

Sauerkraut Production

Staining Reagents

Acid-Fast Stain

Carbol fuchsin (Ziehl's)
Solution A
Basic fuchsin (90% dye content)	0.3 g
Ethyl alcohol (95%)	10.0 ml

Solution B
Phenol	5.0 g
Distilled water	95.0 ml

Note: Mix Solutions A and B. Add 2 drops of Triton X per 100 ml of stain for use in heatless method.

Acid Alcohol
Ethyl alcohol (95%)	97.0 ml
Hydrochloric acid	3.0 ml

Methylene blue
Methylene blue	0.3 g
stilled water	100.0 ml

Capsule Stain

Crystal violet (1%)
Crystal violet (85% dye content)	1.0 g
Distilled water	100.0 ml

Copper sulfate solution (20%)
Copper sulfate ($CuSO_4 \cdot 5H_2O$)	20.0 g
Distilled water	80.0 ml

Fungal Stains

Lactophenol–cotton-blue solution
Lactic acid	20.0 ml
Phenol	20.0 g
Glycerol	40.0 ml
Distilled water	20.0 ml
Aniline blue	0.05 g

Note: Heat gently in hot water (double boiler) to dissolve, then add aniline blue dye.

Water–iodine solution
Gram's iodine (as in Gram's stain)	10.0 ml
Distilled water	30.0 ml

Gram Stain

Crystal violet (Hucker's)
Solution A
Crystal violet (90% dye content)	2.0 g
Ethyl alcohol (95%)	20.0 ml

Solution B
Ammonium oxalate	0.8 g
Distilled water	80.0 ml

Note: Mix Solutions A and B.

Gram's iodine
Iodine	1.0 g
Potassium iodide	2.0 g
Distilled water	300.0 ml

Ethyl alcohol (95%)
Ethyl alcohol (100%)	95.0 ml
Distilled water	5.0 ml

Safranin
Safranin O	0.25 ml
Ethyl alcohol (95%)	10.0 ml
Distilled water	100.0 ml

Negative Stain

Nigrosin
Nigrosin, water-soluble	10.0 g
Distilled water	100.0 ml

Note: Immerse in boiling water bath for 30 minutes.
Formalin	0.5 ml

Note: Filter twice through double filter paper.

Spore Stain

Malachite green
Malachite green	5.0 g
Distilled water	100.0 ml

Safranin
Same as in Gram stain

254

Biochemical Test Reagents

Barritt's reagent, for detection of acetylmethyl-carbinol

Solution A

Alpha-naphthol	5.0 g
Ethanol, absolute	95.0 ml

Note: Dissolve the alpha-naphthol in the ethanol with constant stirring.

Solution B

Potassium hydroxide	40.0 g
Creatine	0.3 g
Distilled water	100.0 ml

Note: Dissolve the potassium hydroxide in 75 ml of distilled water. The solution will become warm. Allow to cool to room temperature. Add the creatine and stir to dissolve. Add the remaining water. Store in a refrigerator.

otin-histidine solution, for Ames test

Iistidine HCl	0.5 mM
Biotin	0.5 mM
Distilled water	10.0 ml

Buffered glycerol (pH 7.2), for immunofluorescence

Glycerin	90.0 ml
Phosphate buffered saline	10.0 ml

Diphenylamine reagent, for detection of nitrates

Dissolve 0.7 g diphenylamine in a mixture of 60 ml concentrated sulfuric acid and 28.8 ml of distilled water. Cool and slowly add 11.3 ml of concentrated hydrochloric acid. Allow to stand for 12 hours. Sedimentation indicates that the reagent is saturated.

Ferric chloride reagent

Ferric chloride	10.0 g
Distilled water	100.0 ml

Gram's iodine, for detection of starch

As in Gram's stain

Hydrogen peroxide, 3%, for detection of catalase activity

Note: Refrigerate when not in use.

Kovac's reagent, for detection of indole

p-Dimethylaminobenzaldehyde	5.0 g
Amyl alcohol	75.0 ml
Hydrochloric acid (concentrated)	25.0 ml

Note: Dissolve the *p*-dimethylaminobenzaldehyde in the amyl alcohol. Add the hydrochloric acid.

McFarland Barium Sulfate Standards, for API® Staph-Ident procedure

Prepare 1% aqueous barium chloride and 1% aqueous sulfuric acid solutions. Using the following table, add the amounts of barium chloride and sulfuric acid to clean 15 × 150-mm screw-capped test tubes. Label the tubes 1 through 10.

Preparation of McFarland Standards

Tube	Barium chloride 1% (ml)	Sulfuric acid 1% (ml)	Corresponding approximate density of bacteria (million/ml)
1	0.1	9.9	300
2	0.2	9.8	600
3	0.3	9.7	900
4	0.4	9.6	1,200
5	0.5	9.5	1,500
6	0.6	9.4	1,800
7	0.7	9.3	2,100
8	0.8	9.2	2,400
9	0.9	9.1	2,700
10	1.0	9.0	3,000

Methyl cellulose, for microscopic observation of protozoa

Methyl cellulose	10.0 g
Distilled water	90.0 ml

Methyl red solution, for detection of acid

Methyl red	0.1 g
Ethyl alcohol	300.0 ml
Distilled water	200.0 ml

Note: Dissolve the methyl red in the 95% ethyl alcohol. Dilute to 500 ml with distilled water.

Nessler's reagent, for detection of ammonia

Potassium iodide   50.0 g
Distilled water (ammonia-free)   35.0 ml
Add saturated aqueous solution of mercuric chloride until a slight precipitate persists.
Potassium hydroxide
  (50% aqueous)   400.0 ml
Note: Dilute to 1000 ml with ammonia-free distilled water. Let stand for 1 week, decant supernatant liquid and store in a tightly capped amber bottle.

Nitrate test solution, for detection of nitrites
Solution A, Sulfanilic acid
  Sulfanilic acid   8.0 g
  Acetic acid, 5 N: 1 part glacial
    acetic acid to 2.5 parts
    distilled water   1000.0 ml
Solution B, Alpha-naphthylamine
  Alpha-naphthylamine   5.0 g
  Acetic acid, 5 N   1000.0 ml

Orthonitrophenyl-β-D-galactoside (ONPG), for enzyme induction
0.1 M sodium phosphate buffer
  (pH 7.0)   50.0 ml
ONPG (8×10^{-4} M)   12.5 mg

p-Aminodimethylaniline oxalate, for detection of oxidase activity
p-Aminodimethylanaline oxalate   0.5 g
Distilled water   50.0 ml
Note: To dissolve fully, gently warm the solution.

Phosphate-buffered saline, 1% (pH 7.2–7.4), for immunofluorescence
Solution A
  Disodium phosphate   1.4 g
  Distilled water   100.0 ml
Solution B
  Sodium dihydrogen phosphate   1.4 g
  Distilled water   100.0 ml
Note: Add 84.1 ml of Solution A to 15.9 ml of Solution B. Add 8.5 g of sodium chloride and q.s. to 1 liter.

Rabbit plasma, for detection of coagulase activity
Note: Store vials at 2°C to 8°C. Reconstitute by the addition of 7.5 ml of sterile water.

Sodium barbital buffer, for immunofluorescence
Sodium barbital   6.98 g
Sodium chloride   6.0 g
1 N hydrochloric acid   27.0 ml
Distilled water, q.s. to 1000 ml

Toluidine blue solution, 0.1%, for detection of DNase activity
1% toluidine blue solution   0.1 ml
Distilled water   99.9 ml

Trommsdorf's reagent, for detection of nitrite
Slowly add 100 ml of 20% aqueous zinc chloride solution to a mixture of 4 g of starch in water. Heat until the starch is dissolved as much as possible and the solution is almost clear. Dilute with water and add 2 g of potassium iodide. Dilute to 1000 ml, filter, and store in an amber bottle.

Bacterial Structure and Staining Techniques

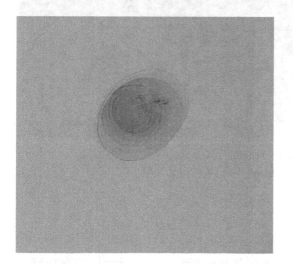

1 A bacterial smear following fixation and staining.

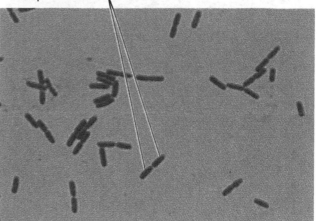

Diplobacilli

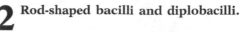

2 Rod-shaped bacilli and diplobacilli.

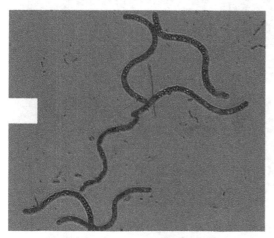

3 Spirilli (spiral-shaped) bacteria.

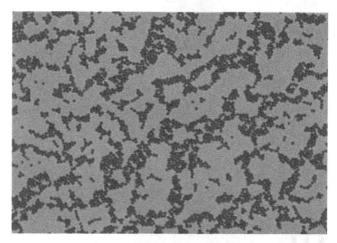

4 Cocci (spherical-shaped) bacteria: S*taphylococcus.*

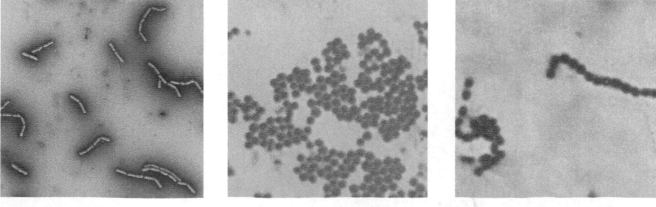

5 **Negative staining:** Bacilli.

6 **Gram stain:** Gram-positive staphylococci. (enlarged view)

7 **Gram stain:** Gram-positive staphylococci. (enlarged view)

Photos 1–5, 8, 9, 11, 14, 15, 20–29, 31, 45, 46, 48, 49, 52, 55, 57, 61–65, 67, 71, 76, 77: From *Microbiology: A Photographic Atlas for the Laboratory,* 1e by Alexander/Strete, © 2001 Benjamin Cummings, an imprint of Addison Wesley Longman, Inc. Reprinted by permission. Photo 47, 79: Courtesy of the Centers for Disease Control. Photo 50 © Jim Solliday/Biological Photo Service. Photo 51: © Carolina Biological Supply/Phototake. Photo 53: © 1990, G.W. Willis/Biological Photo Service. Photo 78: © Leon Lebeau/Custom Medical Stock Photography.

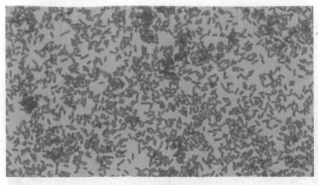

8 **Gram stain:** Gram-negative *E. coli*

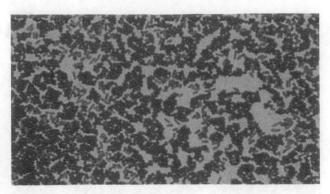

9 **Gram stain:** Gram-negative *E. coli* and Gram-positive staphylococci.

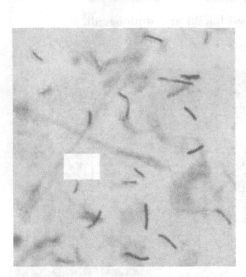

10 **Acid-fast stain:** Acid-fast mycobacteria.

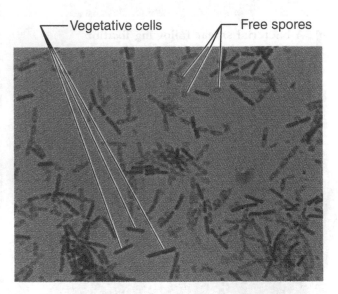

Vegetative cells   Free spores

11 **Spore stain showing free spores and vegetative bacilli.**

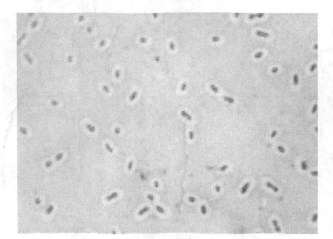

12 **Capsule stain:** Capsulated diplococci.

Media for Growth, Isolation, Differentiation, and Enumeration

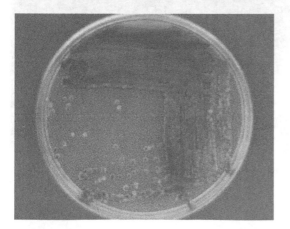

13 **Nutrient agar plate:** Four-way streak-plate inocculation with *Serratia marcescens*.

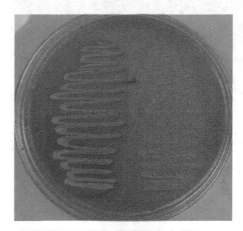

14 **MacConkey agar plate:** Lactose fermenter on left, lactose non-fermenter on right.

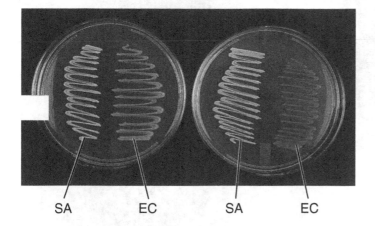

SA   EC   SA   EC

15 **Nutrient agar (left) and phenylethyl alcohol agar (PEA, right):** Each plate inoculated with *Staphylococcus aureus* (SA) and *Escherichia coli* (EC). Gram-negative *E. coli* exhibits reduced grown on PEA.

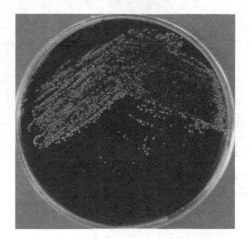

16 **Eosin-methylene blue agar plate:** *E. coli* exhibiting a green metallic sheen.

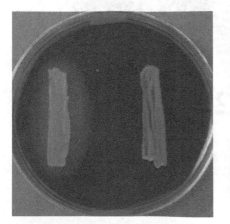

17 **Mannitol salt agar plate:** Mannitol fermenter on left; mannitol non-fermenter on right.

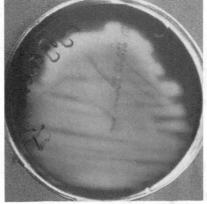

18 **Blood agar plate:** Beta hemolysis.

19 **Blood agar plate:** Alpha hemolysis.

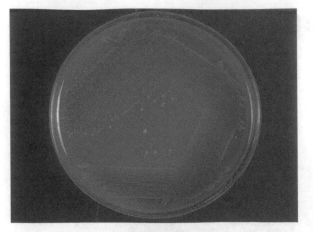

20 **Blood agar plate:** Gamma hemolysis.

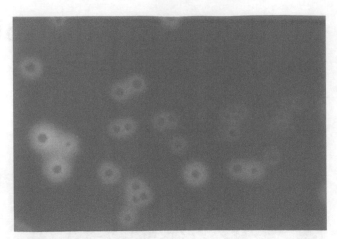

21 **Blood agar plate:** Beta hemolysis.

22 **Blood agar plate:** Alpha hemolysis.

35°C

25°C

5°C

23 Effect of temperature on bacterial growth.

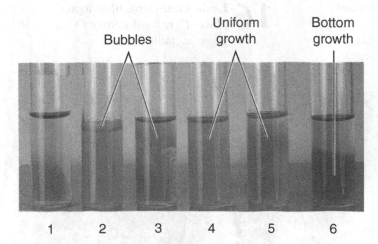

Bubbles   Uniform growth   Bottom growth

1   2   3   4   5   6

24 **Bacterial growth patterns in thioglycollate broth tubes.** Bubbles (tubes 2 and 3) are indicative of gas-producing bacteria; uniform growth (tubes 4 and 5) is indicative of facultative anaerobic bacteria; and bottom growth is indicative of anaerobic bacteria. Tube 1 is the uninoculated control.

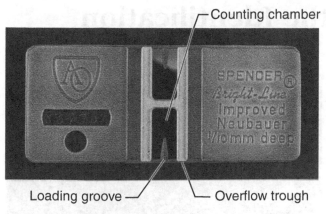

Counting chamber

Loading groove — — Overflow trough

25 Hemocytometer for manual enumeration of bacterial cells.

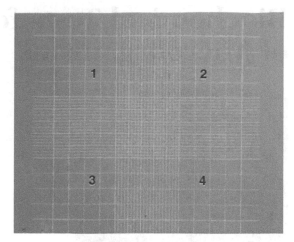

1   2

3   4

26 Microscopic view of hemocytometer chambers for bacterial cell counts (chambers 1–4).

1×10^{-1} 1×10^{-2} 1×10^{-3} 1×10^{-4} 1×10^{-5} 1×10^{-6} 1×10^{-7}

27 Serial dilution of bacterial culture for quantitation of viable cell numbers.

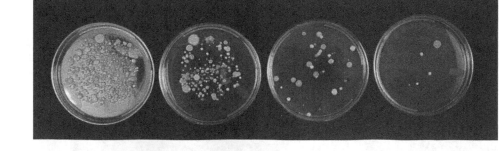

28 Agar plating procedure for viable cell counts using dilutions (left to right) 1×10^3, 1×10^4, 1×10^5, 1×10^6.

29 Counters for the enumeration of bacterial colonies.

Biochemical Tests for the Identification of Microorganisms

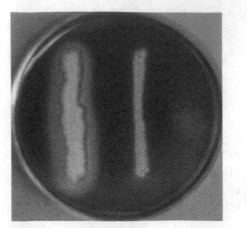

30 **Starch agar plate:** Starch hydrolysis on left; no starch hydrolysis on right.

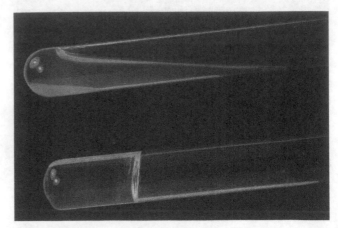

31 **Nutrient gelatin tubes:** Top tube shows gelatin liquefaction, bottom tube negative for gelatin liquefaction.

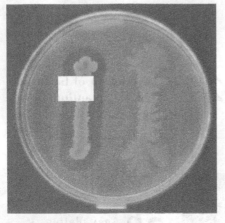
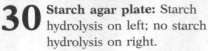

32 **Tributyrin agar plate:** Lipid hydrolysis on left; no lipid hydrolysis on right.

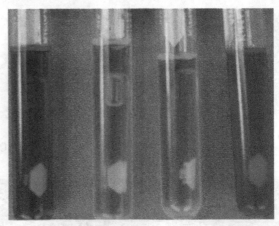

33 **Carbohydrate fermentaion test:** (from left to right) uninoculated, acid and gas, acid, negative.

34 **Triple sugar–iron agar test:** (from left to right) uninoculated; alkaline slant/acid butt, H_2S; alkaline slant/ acid butt; acid slant/acid butt, gas; acid slant/acid butt.

35 **Indole production test:** (from left to right) uninoculated, negative, positive.

36 **Methyl red test:** (from left to right) uninoculated, positive, negative.

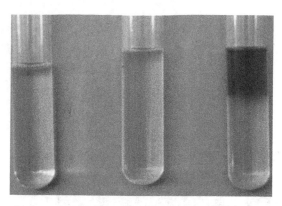

37 **Voges-Proskauer test:** (from left to right) uninoculated, negative, positive.

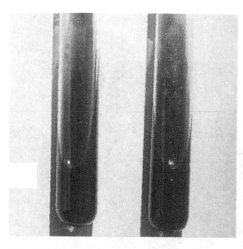

38 **Citrate utilization test:** positive on left, negative on right.

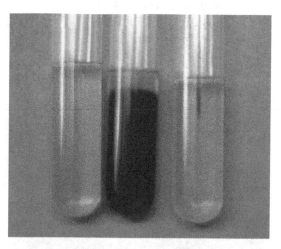

39 **Hydrogen sulfide production test:** (from left to right) negative, positive with motility, positive with no motility.

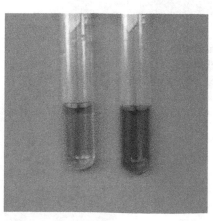

40 **Urease test:** negative on left; positive on right.

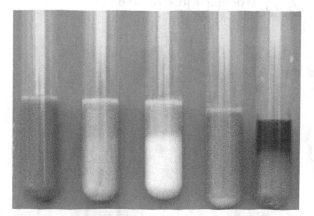

41 **Litmus milk reactions:** (from left to right) uninoculated, acid, acid with reduction and curd, alkaline, proteolysis.

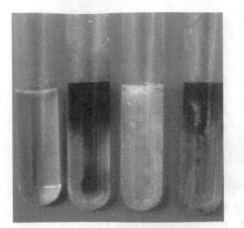

42 Nitrate reduction test: (from left to right) uninoculated, positive with Solutions A + B, positive with Solutions A + B + zinc powder, negative with Solutions A + B + zinc powder.

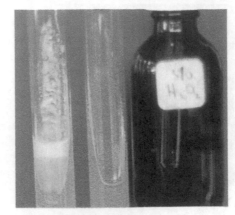

43 Catalase test: Positive on the left, as evidenced by the evolution of O$_2$ bubbles; negative on the right.

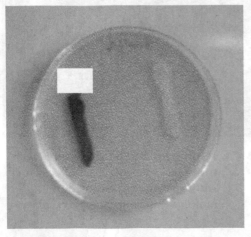

44 Oxidase test: Positive on the left, negative on the right.

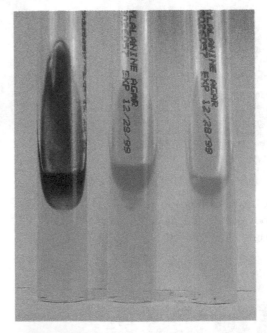

45 Phenylalanine deaminase test: (from left to right) positive, negative, uninoculated.

46 Decarboxylase test: (from left to right) lysine decarboxylase positive, lysine decarboxylase negative, uninoculated.

Protozoa and Fungi

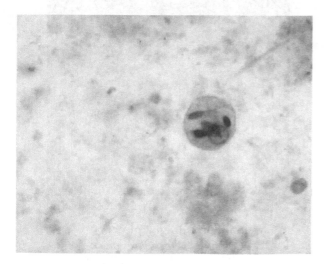

47 *Entamoeba histolytica:* Causative of amoebic dysentery.

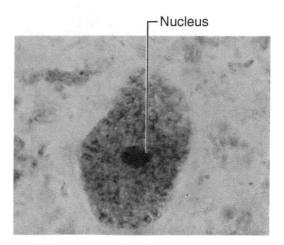

Nucleus

48 A trophozoite of the amoeboid protozoan *Entamoeba hystolica.*

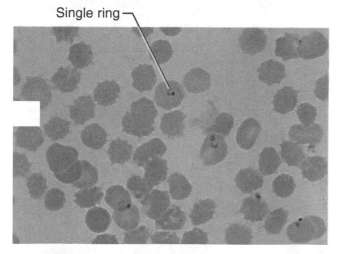

Single ring

49 Red blood cells infected by the ring stage (signet ring) of *Plasmodium vivax,* the causative agent of malaria.

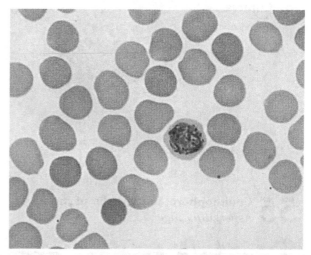

50 *Plasmodium vivax:* Malarial parasite.

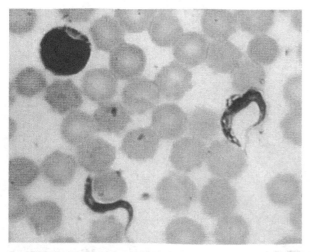

51 *Trypanosoma gambiense:* Causative agent for African sleeping sickness.

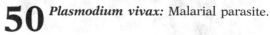
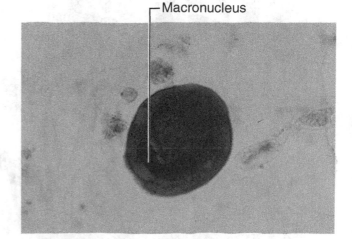

Macronucleus

52 A cyst of the ciliated protozoan *Balantidium coli.* The cysts are spherical and lack surface cilia. The macronucleus is visible in this photo.

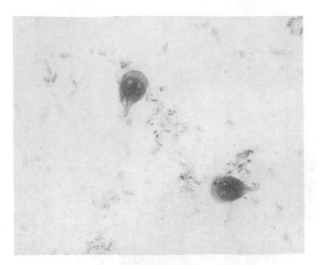

53 *Giardia lamblia:* Causative agent of gastrointestinal diarrhea.

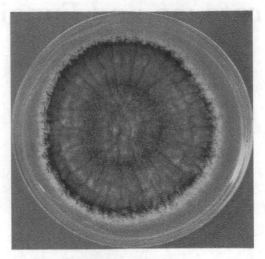

54 Sabouraud agar plate: Colony of *Aspergillus niger.*

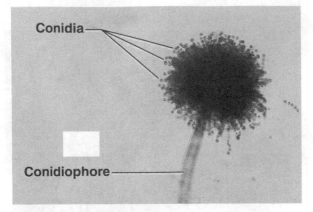

Conidia

Conidiophore

55 Conidiophore and conidia of mold *Aspergillus niger.*

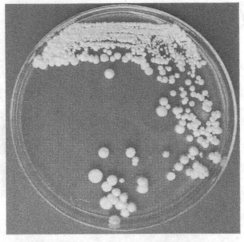

56 *Saccharomyces cerevisiae:* Colonies of yeast cells.

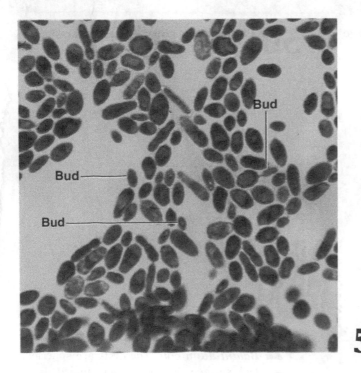

Bud

Bud

Bud

57 *Saccharomyces cerevisiae:* Microscopic cell structure.

Antibiotic and Disinfectant Activities

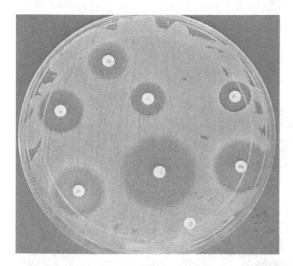

58 Kirby-Bauer antibiotic susceptibility test.

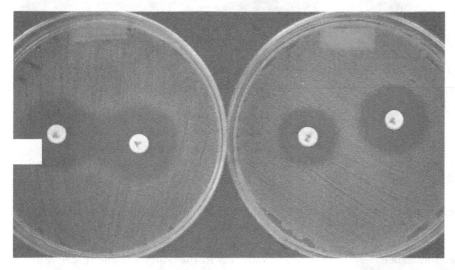

59 Synergistic effects of drug combinations: Synergism on the left, no synergism on the right.

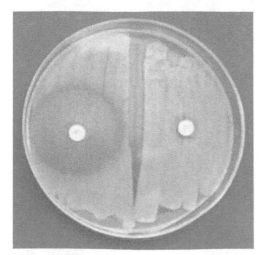

60 Penicillinase activity: Penicillin-sensitive on left, penicillin-resistant on right.

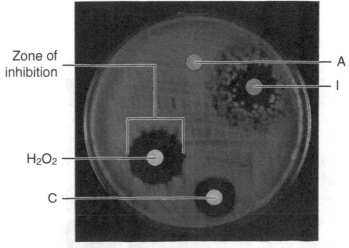

Zone of inhibition

A

I

H₂O₂

C

61 Antibiotic susceptibility test with discs saturated with chlorine bleach (C), hydrogen peroxide (H₂O₂), isopropyl alcohol (A), and tincture of iodine (I).

Microbiology of Water

Durham tube

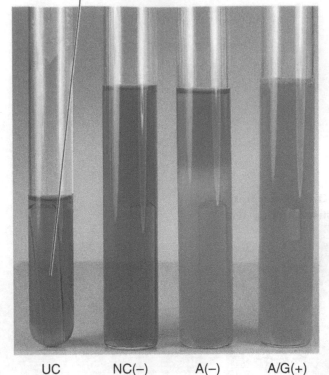

UC   NC(−)   A(−)   A/G(+)

62 **P   e MNP presumptive test results:** (from left to right), uninoculated control (UC); inoculated tube, no change (NC); inoculated tube, acid production only (A); inoculated tube, acid and gas production (A/G). Only the tube on the right (A/G) is considered positive; the other inoculated tubes (NC and A) are considered negative.

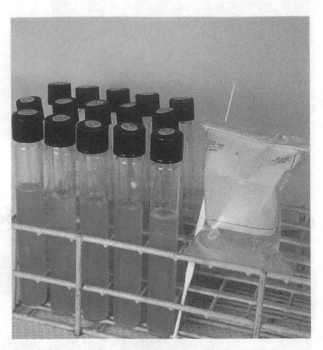

63 **The MPN presumptive test results for a water sample.** There were five positives (acid and gas) for the 10 ml tubes in the front row, five positives for the 1 ml tubes in the middle row, and five negatives (acid only) in the back row. The score (5, 5, 0) indicates 240 coliforms per 100 ml of water. This represents a positive presumptive test for the presence of coliforms in the water sample under test.

64 **Membrane filter method for quantitative water analysis for enumeration of coliform bacteria.**

Medical Microbiology and Immunology

Epithelial cell — G(+) rods — G(+) streptococci

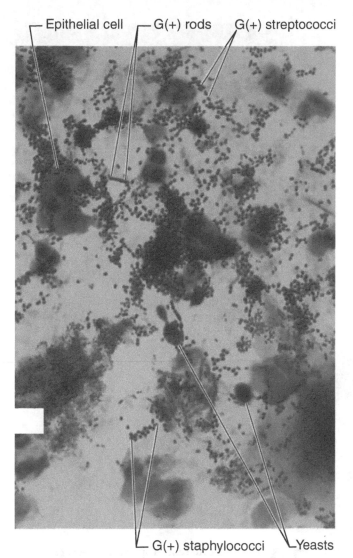

G(+) staphylococci — Yeasts

65 A Gram stain of teeth scrapings.

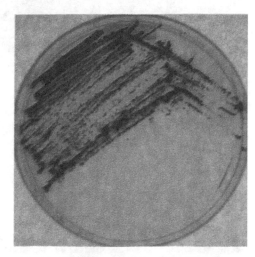

66 Tinsdale or Mueller-Hinton tellurite agar plate: Positive for the presence of diphtheroids.

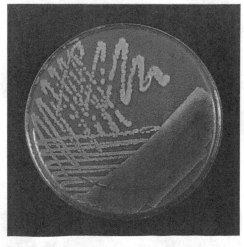

67 Chocolate agar plate: Four-way streak, throat culture.

Identification of Staphylococcal Pathogens

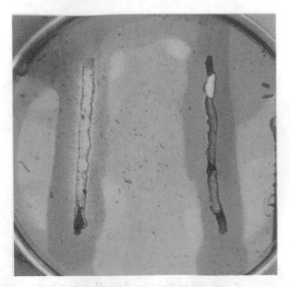

68 **DNase agar plate:** Positive on the left; negative on the right.

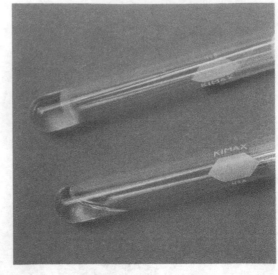

69 **Coagulase test:** Negative on the bottom, positive on the top.

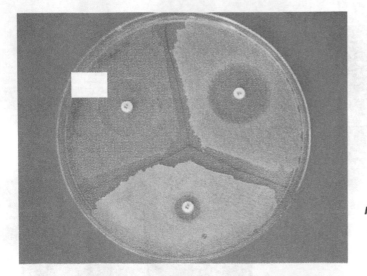

70 **Novobiocin test:** Top: *Staphylococcus aureus, Staphylococcus epidermis*—sensitive. Bottom: *Staphylococcus saprophyticus*—resistant.

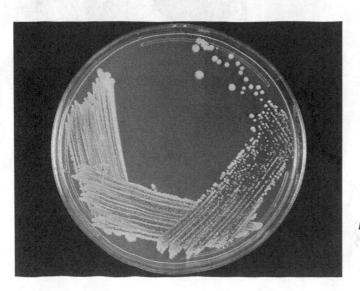

71 **Streak-plate of *Staphylococcus aureus:*** Note the circular, convex, smooth, and cream-colored to golden-yellow appearance.

Identification of Streptococcal Pathogens

72 **6.5% Sodium chloride test:**
Group D enterococcus on left,
Group D nonenterococcus on right.

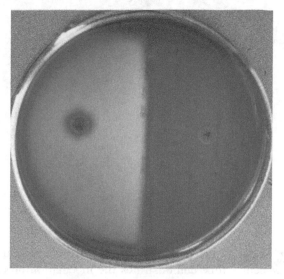

73 **Bacitracin test:** Positive for
beta-hemolytic group A streptococci
on the left, negative on the right.

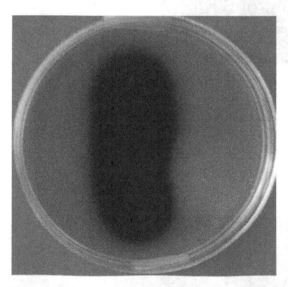
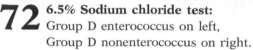

74 **Bile esculin agar plate:** Positive for
Group D streptococci.

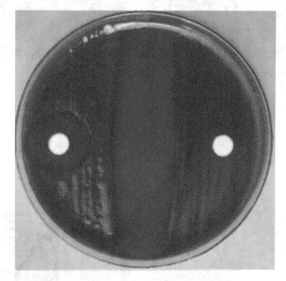

75 **Optochin test:** Alpha-hemolytic
S. pneumoniae on the left, other
alpha-hemolytic streptococcal species
on right.

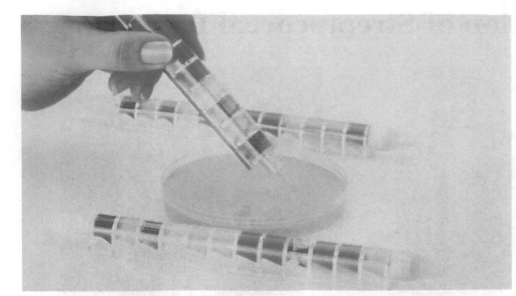

76 **Enterotube multitest system.** Rear tube is uninoculated control. The center tube demonstrates the inoculation procedure, and the front tube is inoculated with the test organism.

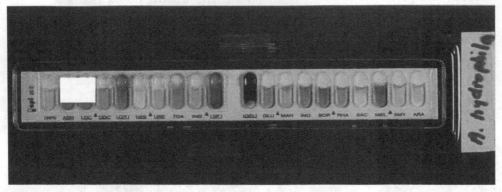

77 **API multitest system.**

78 **Agglutination reaction:** Positive on left, negative on right.

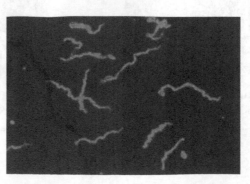

79 **Bacterial immunofluorescence.**